The Nature of Man

and the

Meaning of Existence

The Nature of Man
and the
Meaning of Existence

By
HAROLD SAXTON BURR, Ph.D.

E. K. Hunt Professor of Anatomy, Emeritus
Yale University School of Medicine

CHARLES C THOMAS • PUBLISHER
Springfield • Illinois • U. S. A.

CHARLES C THOMAS • PUBLISHER
BANNERSTONE HOUSE
301-327 East Lawrence Avenue, Springfield, Illinois, U.S.A.

With THOMAS BOOKS careful attention is given to all details of manufacturing and design. It is the Publisher's desire to present books that are satisfactory as to their physical qualities and artistic possibilities and appropriate for their particular use. THOMAS BOOKS will be true to those laws of quality that assure a good name and good will.

Printed in the United States of America

ACKNOWLEDGMENTS

THIS BOOK has been made possible through the generous cooperation of the Yale University School of Medicine, Mr. William Perry Bentley of Dallas, Texas, and Mr. and Mrs. Halsted Myers of Old Lyme, Connecticut. It is not possible to detail all the help derived from a multitude of sources.

H.S.B.

CONTENTS

The Nature of Man

and the

Meaning of Existence

Chapter I

THE NOTION OF UNIVERSE

THE TERM, Universe, literally translated, means to turn into a whole. Through the centuries, this has implied a unitary characteristic of all that is observable by man through his own senses and the attendant brain. In modern times, the range of things seen by the eye and understood by the mind, has been greatly extended by improved optics and the development of modern electronics. Bigger and better telescopes have enabled us to see farther into outer space. More perfect microscopes have penetrated deeper into the structure of nature. The modern radio tube, with its capacity to send and receive radiations of manifold frequencies, has given further insight into the enormity of space and the complexity of the infinitely small. As a result, there is available an enormous amount of detail, multifarious in kind and overwhelming in complexity; but real understanding of the true nature and meaning of the Universe is still to come. There are some who hold that it is a closed system, perhaps infinite in extent, yet having an outer limit. Others maintain that it is steadily expanding, ever moving away from the observer. Yet the notion that the Universe is an entity, a whole, which possesses properties that can be studied, seems to be held devotedly by men of science in all parts of the world. This implies that there are regularities in the cosmos that can be described and recognized in place and time. It is surprising that in the face of such an immense collection of detailed observations, some hold fast to the idea that despite the regularities, the chief characteristic of the Universe is chaos. Thus the laws of probability are sufficient to explain the observables; the only order that exists is created by the mind of man!

A healthy respect for man's brains still balks at the notion that man can create order out of chaos, can put order and describable

3

entities into chaos. The mind of man has well-nigh incredible potentialities, but that it can, out of chaos, order the sun and moon and stars in their courses, would seem to be outside of even its capacities. Rather, it would seem to be a more likely assumption to hold that the Universe is a place of Law and Order that the mind of man can hopefully discover. Admittedly, the time during which man has explored that which lies both within and without is but a minuscule fragment of the possible ten billion years of the estimated life of the cosmos. From a commonsense angle, most of us believe that the sun will rise to-morrow, that the North Star can be identified on any clear night. Moreover, we stake our lives on these observations. We traverse the sea and the heavens because of these phenomena. We thrust ourselves into the unknown, because we know as a matter of experience, that we can rely on them. We know that the stars, the planets, the galaxies, occupy a certain position in space to-day and, by calculation, it can be predicted where they will be to-morrow, or a hundred, or ten thousand years from now.

To be sure, the physicists have demonstrated that in the infinitely small, it is virtually impossible to describe adequately the shape, size and movements in time of the entities. Thus there is uncertainty and indeterminancy at the heart of the microcosm. To many, it follows, therefore, that the Universe is essentially unpredictable and hence chaotic. But in the history of scientific discovery when an apparent impossibility is met, the creative imagination of the mind of man uncovers a new key which unlocks one of the seemingly sealed doors. It may well be that the uncertainty is not real, but rather is a sign of the lack of knowledge, for it is strikingly clear that knowledge is still woefully incomplete. This, of course, is the inspiration of Science. There is so much to be discovered. It may well be that as our knowledge and understanding increase, uncertainty may ultimately disappear. Thus, the argument that the uncertainty principle underpins the doctrine of "Free Will" may have to be abandoned. Instead, it may be that the apparent chaos in the cosmos will be replaced by the discovery of the law and order that is describable, reproducible, and predictable not only in the area of the almost infinitely large, but also in the realm of the infinitely small.

If the assumption, that the Universe is orderly, is accepted, the vital question arises, What holds the cosmos together? In other words, what is the "glue" that keeps the whole from flying apart? It must be obvious that in a place of law and order, not only must the entities be described and located, but also the necessary relatedness between them established. The forces which maintain these orderly relationships must likewise be determined. The sun and the moon, the stars, the planets and the earth must be described and their position and movement in space established. Equally important is the nature of the forces which maintain the necessary relatednesses between all the describable components. Moreover, not only must these forces be rigorously determined, but also there must be equal certainty concerning the way these obviously powerful forces transmit their effects. It is generally agreed that gravitation is one of these characteristic controls of necessary relationships. Much is known about the consequences of gravitation. The apple falls to the ground; Lunik III orbits the moon and the earth: but what gravitation is and how it is transmitted is still to be determined. So, also, is the whole spectrum of radiation. The sun showers space with bullets of light — photons, electrons, and so on. Radio, T-V, radar — all sorts of man-made radiations are sent hither and yon; but the medium, the substance, the stuff by means of which the "vibrations" move is still an enigma. Ever since the cosmologists and the physicists compelled the abandonment of the theory of an all-enveloping Ether, search for a more valid substitute has been pursued. Out of the East has come the intuitive assumption of a Continuum, but a rigorous definition has not accompanied the idea. And yet the idea is compelling and perhaps its nature can be determined, for one of the interesting characteristics of the Universe is the pervading presence of electrical phenomena. In fact, a distinguished physicist has defined electricity as "the way Nature behaves." And there must be something in this, for a large part of contemporary civilization is distinguished by the application of the laws of electricity to the design and construction of instruments and machines, ranging from light sources to nuclear energy. It turns up everywhere, often in unsuspected places. It is the basis of the atomic series. It determines the relationships between atoms, thus establishing the describable regularities of the world and cosmos around us. It is the core of all chemical reactions. Finally, it provides a factor of prime importance to any understanding of Nature; it gives direction to the forces at work. If law and order exist, then directive forces must be present to relate the ultimate entities, be they mass or energy, into specific arrangements that exist in time and which can be predicted. It is well-known that if the atoms — hydrogen and oxygen — are brought together under the proper conditions, water results. This is essentially an electrical process. Furthermore, if a voltage or potential difference exists between any two points — on a conducting wire, for example — a movement of electrons occurs through the wire, thus producing an electrical current. This elementary fact is of great theoretical and practical importance, but a corollary is of even greater value. The flow of current from high to low potential establishes in the immediate vicinity of the wire an electrical field, an *electrodynamic field,* stretching out a measurable distance from the conductor itself. Thus, there is set up a force which determines the position and movements of all the charged entities within the field. An example of this is the well-established fact that the direction in which a compass needle points can be altered by bringing it into the field produced by passing an electrical current through a coil of wire.

It is not surprising, therefore, that as was suggested some decades ago, the Universe is essentially an electrodynamic field. Such a field is conceived as sets of electrical forces, establishing all the describable entities in determined positions controlling the direction and momentum of all movement. Thus, electricity is Nature. This is an assumption on a grand scale and much needs to be done to verify it. Fortunately, there are masses of evidence supporting the idea; relatively few, if any, contradictions. This is particularly true of the non-living aspects of Nature, but the existence of field forces in the living world has only recently been postulated. To be sure, heart waves, brain waves, muscle potentials, and electrical correlates of the transmission of impulses through nerves has long been recognized; but that living things, because of demonstrable voltage gradients, also exhibit electrodynamic field properties, is a relatively recent notion. Such an idea has merit in that under the field postulate all the electrical phenomena detectable in living organisms can be subsumed. It has further value in that it brings all living things, from amoeba to man, into the same frame of reference as the rest of the Universe. This is particularly important, for it has long been recognized that the building blocks, of which every living thing is composed, are identical with those of the material world. If the electrodynamic field controls the position and movement of charged elements in the physical world, then the same charged components of the living world should obey the same forces. Hence, it follows that life is not some special "creation." It is not only in the Universe, but of it and, therefore, subject to the laws of the Universe in the same manner as the stars in their courses. This conclusion is often labeled authoritarian, dictatorial, dogmatic and is anathema to the vanity of Man who delights to believe that he is master of his soul and of the world around him. He resents the thought of restraints imposed by forces he does not understand. He much prefers to think of himself as a free agent, free to do as he pleases without reference to anything outside of himself. As a result, he has erected the dualistic concept, that while his body may be subject to Natural Law he, as a living human being, possesses a soul which is over and above such arbitrary rules, is subject only to the Moral Law. Thus, he is a special creation — in the Universe, but not of it. This demands belief in a Creator who can step into the Universe at will for his own purposes. Thus, man would hold that a field theory of the Universe implies an impersonal, cold, mechanical cosmos. Many find this difficult to accept. And yet, much time and thought have been devoted over the years to specification of the development and evolution of the Universe from its primary collision of two protons to its present and probably future complexity. So also has the development and evolution of living things been subject to extensive examination. These two processes have never ceased. They are continuing and, so far as anyone can see, will continue into the unforseeable future.

Since the term, "evolution," implies growth and change from the relatively simple to the increasingly complex, patterns emerge making it possible to discriminate stages in a continuing process. In the cosmos the stars and the planets can be described because they exhibit characteristic arrangements of their component entities. These complexes of atoms, moreover, can be seen to change — a new star is born. Originally, possibly quite simple in organization, in time the star becomes larger and more complex until it exhibits an arrangement of parts peculiar to itself. Stars can be described and classified. They certainly are not static but present evidences of change within their particular framework. They grow, they change and, in all possibility, eventually disappear or die. To argue that the necessary relatednesses which impose such patterns and control such changes are chaotic, is not tenable. There must be law and order in the material cosmos, or such things simply could not be.

It must be obvious, furthermore, that the changes in the observable Universe cannot be accounted for on chance alone. There is a process, a progression that is not helter-skelter but rather exhibits direction. The movement is from the simple to the more and more complex, from single entities to combinations of larger numbers of units. As a result, organizations of atoms appear which exhibit unique and individual properties. Thus, the sun can be described as different from the moon, the earth as different from the North Star. New entities are constantly being created, new combinations continuously appear replacing those which have been born, grown-up and died. But through the whole process there is discernable a pattern, a schema, a recognizable organization. This describable arrangement exists, however, in the face of a constant and seemingly chaotic flux. Some patterning of forces must be at work to preserve form in the midst of change. Such forces must be everywhere operative throughout the cosmos. It is such forces that constitute the Natural Law, the regulatory controls which impose order upon the Universe.

All that has been said about the material Universe is equally applicable to the living world. Living things, likewise, begin as relatively simple arrays of atoms, arrays which grow into the greater and greater complexities with new properties of adaptation to the changing environment, and the possibly unique capacity for self-reproduction. Here, also, order can be found in the face of constant chemical change, order which persists in time, though the components of that order come and go. The entities, furthermore, which are built into the formed living being are the same components which make up the material world. The entities, the components, the building blocks are everywhere the same throughout the entire Universe, including all forms of life wherever they may be found. This means the particular kind of life we find on the speck of dust we call the earth, lost as it is in the immensity of space, need not be the only kind of life existent. Other specks may also show an order imposed by Natural Law of a somewhat different sort from our familiar plants and animals.

It cannot be emphasized too strongly that it is the presence of Natural Law — gravitation, the laws of physics and chemistry, of electricity and magnetism — which makes it possible for the Universe to exist, for living beings to live. Were these laws not definable, not in some measure understood, existence would be impossible. It is not surprising that the early scientists, recognizing order in all that lay about them, sought explanations which would satisfy the current knowledge. From the time of the Greeks to the present day, the imagination of the mind of man has erected theories to account for constancy. Many of these have invoked non-definable agents, entelechies, *élan vitals,* souls, minds, spirits and, most recently, the forces included in cybernetics. These steering forces, guiding agents, directing the material and the living during the process of growth and change, all imply that the evolution of the Universe and of living things has direction, that the components are going somewhere.

It is an interesting fact that virtually all the forces we know, forces which mankind has learned to work with, have directional or vector properties. None of man's mastery of physics and chemistry would be possible without such knowledge. The directional or vector forces, moreover, about which we know most, are electrical in character. It is admitted, of course, that gravitation is such a force. Perhaps, also, it will ultimately be understood in electrical terms.

The assumption that Law and Order obtain in the Universe seems unescapable. Unless this were so, it would be impossible to describe anything living or dead, nor could we predict sunrise and sunset, the position of the stars, eclipses, the lunar cycle, let alone the passage of time. But these are central facts in the Universe. Man has not made them, though he has discovered some of them. Having discovered them, he has learned to work with them. When he does, great things result. When he ignores them, disaster follows.

Unfortunately, there is another set of laws—man-made. These have grown like Topsy, to bewitch and bewilder man down through the ages. Invented by man to control other men, they are monuments to the inherent vanity and lust for power which seem to be unfortunate characteristics of man. To be sure, we are unruly. To be sure, we tread on other's toes. Certainly we strive to get ahead and, too often, we care not what happens to those who get in our way. Although we cannot solve our own personal problems, we insist on solving others' difficulties. We do not behave any too well ourselves, yet we force others to behave not as we do, but as we say. We make and enforce laws for others, too often ignoring them ourselves, if they are inconvenient.

Again, unfortunately, these man-made controls which are designed to force human behavior into stereotyped conformity, bear no relation to the Natural Law of the Universe. In fact, these products of the mind of man often contravene Nature. Thus, there exist two set of laws — side-by-side — one inherent in the nature of the Universe, the other man-made for mankind. Law, therefore, means many things to many people. To most of us, it means the written law, the body of rules and regulations erected by legislatures and courts. Also written, but established by religious bodies, is the moral law. Both are attempts by human beings to control human behavior; in the first instance of others, in the second, of ourselves and others. Both result from the fact that the problem of human relations remains unsolved. Man still has no clear idea of who or what he is, what he is here for, what his true relationship is to the Universe in which he finds himself. We seem to be very little better off than was primitive man. We still fight each other individually and collectively; all this in spite of pages and pages of written religious and secular law.

Then, too, in addition to the innumerable rules and regulations found in books, is the living law, the rules of conduct individuals and groups develop as a result of some partially envisaged philosophy of living. There is no necessary relationship between these two attempts to control behavior. No central theory exists from which these controls can be deduced. It is not surprising that there should be so much confusion, so much divergence, so much conflict. That which is illegal in the Western world may be permissible in Eastern civilizations. The good or right behavior in Central Africa is wrong in London, Paris, or New York.

It can be argued that at the heart of the problem is the sense of values. But who among us can define the good, the true, and the beautiful in such terms as to be generally accepted or useful throughout the world? Values are largely culturally determined and, therefore, differ as widely as the backgrounds from which they stem. Yet, it has been argued forcefully by theologians, philosophers, and teachers that man is man wherever you happen to find him. Man is man, whether he be found as an aborigine or in the best civilization we know.

There should be some universals, therefore, some general properties that can be seen to run through all legal systems. Are there such? We simply do not know; again, because we have not answered the age-old question, "What Is Man, That Thou Art Mindful Of Him?" While it cannot be gainsaid that all human beings are physically alike, it is equally true that every individual exhibits characteristics that set him apart from all others. Why is this? From the dawn of history man has attempted to answer this question by asserting that while physically he is like all others, nevertheless, he is endowed with a soul, a spirit, which is uniquely different from that of others and which gives man an extra-natural character. This is the dualistic approach, almost univers-ally accepted, that man is a special creation of a Divine Being.

And yet, can this be true? For it assumes that from some source outside the living organism, a something which cannot be seen, heard nor handled, which defies definition, sets up the individual, guiding and directing all of its activities. There appears, therefore, the supernatural, the existence of forces, of controls over and above the physical or material. Thus the Universe is not a study, but rather a diversity. Man, then, is a special creation in the Universe, but not of it; a physical system to be sure but, nevertheless, controlled by factors not a part of the Universe, but superior to it. These forces, however, which accomplish this cannot be shown to exist in space, nor in time, nor to involve energy transformations. How, then, can they affect the physical body which does occupy space, does exist in time, and does involve energy transformations? How can this be when everything else we know about the Universe makes it abundantly clear that every single entity exhibits the existence of definable law and a recognizable order? The Universe is a place of law and order which the mind of man can discover and, hopefully, understand.

To assume that there are forces which are supernatural is to denigrate the Universe. This notion has arisen out of the vanity and ignorance of man. It ignores the Natural Law, the Law of the Universe, the law which determines the stars in their courses and without which not a single thing we recognize, including ourselves, could exist for the fraction of a second. It would substitute for the law that keeps the Universe together, man-made dicta which, while serving pragmatically in the absence of knowledge to make man behave, yet, nevertheless, are at variance with the Universe in which man exists. To some degree, this might be useful, for our knowledge is little and our ignorance great. Possibly, some man-made laws can serve as a crutch to keep us from falling while we struggle to gain more knowledge and understanding.

Both the Written Law and the Moral Law, moreover, are full of must-nots and do-nots. Man, in his egotism, is quite sure he knows what the other fellow should do, or not do. He knows because he believes that he is endowed with free-will, the ability to make choices, discriminations, decisions and be guided, he hopefully believes, by some Higher Power. Hence, he examines the Written Law of the past and bends it to his idea of what is right; or he studies the long history of that revealed law which has come to prophets and sages over the years, and draws up a set of regulations which he proceeds to impose on others.

Looked at from this point of view, man-made law has not been particularly successful. It is highly doubtful if any real advance has been made in the control of Human Behavior since the beginning of recorded history, and for a good and sufficient reason. We have been attacking this crucial problem from the wrong angle. We have been sold a bill of goods by religionists and lawyers alike. Being unsure ourselves, being well-aware of our own ignorance and lack of understanding, we have bowed down to those assertive ones who claimed to have had the answers. The result has been confusion worse confounded; hot wars, cold wars, crime and delinquency until, for many, there is no longer any reason for optimism.

But that is absurd. Man has survived all these crippling attitudes because he is the result of the operation of Natural Law. It is very easy to forget, or to overlook and take for granted the fact that we are what we are, that we can survive this muddle only because our bones and muscles, our hearts and lungs, our nerves and brains have resulted from the action of forces which are the Natural Law and Order of the Universe. Man did not dream up this Law, he discovered it; or at least he has discovered some of it. The Universe exhibits law and order; so does man. Were this not so, we could not tell a cat from a dog, a man from a monkey, nor one human being from another. In other words, the Universe, and everything in it exhibits a pattern of organization, a characteristic arrangement of the component entities. There are many who maintain that this is sheer accident, that the Universe is chaos, that the only order in it is that which is put into it by the mind of man. Some have held, and still hold, that it is much easier to grasp the idea of a Universe of chaos than it is one of Law. There are so many unknowns in an orderly Universe that it is impossible, in all probability, to know or to understand it. So it is held — Why bother? Man has a brain; let him put order in chaos. Truly, man has a brain or, perhaps more correctly, man is a brain. He is a marvellously constructed entity. Because his brain is made up of more than ten billion components, it has qualitative attributes that endow each and everyone of us with miraculous capacities, capacities so numerous, so phenomenal, that only very rarely does any one individual ever realize more than a fraction of his capabilities. Perhaps it is because of this enormous potential that man has decided that he, like Papa, "knows best." But he forgets that he did not make his body nor his brain. He did not design the fabric of bone and muscle. He did not devise the heart and the transport system of blood vessels. He did not create the brain, of which the mind is a qualitative attribute. Not only has he not done so, there is little sign that he ever can do so, unless he learns a great deal more about the Natural Law which has made him.

This is the Law that man must know. If, in the interim during which his ignorance is so great, he has to create man-made laws to protect man from himself, let every effort be made to tie temporary regulations to the best we know of fundamental law.

It would seem logical, therefore, that the problem of the laws relating to human behavior should be attacked by the same methods which have made it possible for man to acquire an enormous control over his physical environment. We have learned much about the operation of the Natural Law in earth, in sky, and sea. By putting this body of Law to work, we make toasters, washing-machines, automobiles, airplanes, ships and submarines, to say nothing of computers which, in some ways, mimic the activities of the brain. Man has been able to accomplish this because he has learned something of the forces and laws that operate in rocks and metals, in air and water, in atoms and molecules. Man, from the beginning, has been a designer of tools, instruments, and machines all of which have made it easier for him to stay alive in a very complex environment. In many senses of the word, he has conquered the earth and, currently, is striving to add space,

or the rest of the Universe, to his armamentarium. It is not surprising that he is rather set-up by all his successes. In his vanity, he
thinks that He has done all these things. Who is this He? Who-
ever he is, he has not lifted himself by his own bootstraps. He
has not created these manifold and wondrous things. He cannot
pat himself on the back and cry, "What a Great Man am I." And
yet, that is the basic assumption underlying the living law, providing the very foundations by which we live. Many believe that
all this has been accomplished through man's unaided will to
achieve. But how has this come about? If you believe in ghosts,
witches, gremlins and God-given souls which may, on occasion,
dwell for a period of time in a physical body, then man is a creative giant who can command the wind and the waves to do his
will. But can he? Obviously, he cannot. He did not invent the
atom; he discovered it. He did not create the law of gravity. He
did not define the laws of intermolecular action. He uncovered
all these things in the world around him. They were there, exhibiting the operation of the law and order of the Universe.

How has this been accomplished? The stock answer, of course,
is that man has a mind, that he is a thinking, reasoning being.
But what is this mind that it can accomplish all these things? If
you hold that mind is some supernatural something which, from
without, guides the destiny of the individual, then you must
throw up your hands, for this is the basic assumption underlying
all of our current failures. This kind of a mind cannot be studied,
for it does not exist in fact. We know it only through the inter-
pretation my mind makes of the actions or behavior engendered
by your mind. Two unknowns, and no equation. The concept of
a supernatural "mind" leads to nothing but futility, and that is
about where we are when we try to solve the problem of human
relations through the activities of an extra-material mind.

This sounds hopeless or pessimistic, but it need not be if we
look at this from a different angle. Admittedly, man has accomplished great things in the material world. Many of us have
"never had it so good." Parts of the world have an unbelievable
standard of material living. Much of this has come about in a

few centuries, a droplet of time in the immensity of Universal time.

The answer, of course, is clear. It is the mind of man that has done these things. But, most emphatically, not the supernatural mind. The mind to which credit must be given is the mind which is the result of the integrated activity of billions of nerve cells which, in critically determined arrangements, comprise the nervous system of man. In other words, the mind of man is the verifiable correlate of the functioning of the nerve cells arranged in a particular pattern of organization. Just so, the redness of the rose is the verifiable correlate of the particular arrangement of the chemical constituents of the rose petal. When two elements are united in a unique relationship, new qualities appear which are not present in either component. So, when billions of entities, the nerve cells, are combined in specific patterns, innumerable qualities—miraculous qualities—attend their activities.

But these entities are not patterned by chance. The nerve cells themselves are organized collections of a very few simple chemicals. The living substance of a nerve is incredibly complex; a mixture of these elementary particles so organized, so multifarious that we still know distressingly little of the details. But we do know that the simple chemicals are related to each other in lawful and understandable ways. The nerve cells are the consequence of the operation of rigid, predictable laws of the Universe —the Natural Law.

In like manner, nerve cells organized by Law are related to each other by similar, precise, definable, powerful laws. It follows, therefore, that the nervous system of man, as well as all other parts of his physical being, are the product of the interaction of Natural Law and material things. Since mind is the qualitative correlate of the law-determined nervous system, moreover, then behavior, which is the result of the activity of that nervous system, must also be law-determined. It would seem only intelligent, then, to examine human behavior as also law-determined.

This must mean, quite obviously, that the answer to the question of why we do what we do should be sought using the same methods man has employed in the conquest of the material world.

The procedure has been somewhat deified by the term, "The Method of Science." In general, as a matter of fact, this method is followed by all of us in adjusting to our environment. The memories of our experience and that of others lead us to guess that if we make a particular assumption, certain consequences will follow; so we bet on the Yankees, or buy Standard Oil. If the results pan out, we hold that our guess was good. So the musician composes his symphony, the writer completes his book, the artist paints his pictures. The guesses are tested pragmatically in the resulting experience. The scientist does the same thing, but adds the very important step of first working out as many of the logical consequences of his assumption or guess, as possible, subjecting the results to experimental verification. In the physical world, adequate controls of the experiments can be achieved. In the world of living things, this is not so easy, but it does not mean that it must not be attempted. The success of science in the analysis of material things has been so phenomenal that there is every reason to believe that equal achievements can be attained in the world of human beings.

It should be reasonably obvious, therefore, that man is caught between the Natural Law (it has made him) and Man-made Law, and there is no necessary relationship between the two. This is the origin of human conflict. He knows that he cannot defy the law that made him, but he often circumvents man-made law. Pulled in one direction by the universals of existence, and in another by the regulations of society, no wonder he is troubled and confused. Since the dawn of history he has been fumbling for an answer. Instead of seeking it in the nature of the Universe, and of man in particular, he has, in his vanity, invented rules of conduct which he calls the Moral Law and set it above and often in conflict with the Universe.

There are universals, of course, in the Natural Law, so the business of man-made law should be a search for the universals in behavior, to build a solid foundation upon which the uniqueness of each individual can be erected with the certainty of adequate results. Not one of us knows enough to predict how this could be done, or what the outcome would be. Not one of us knows enough to define what bits of information should reach the storehouse of memory and what should be eliminated. For we do not know what is good. We have fixed ideas about the bad, and there is no universal character to our value judgment, because we set up our own standards without reference to the Universe in which we find ourselves. There is only one measure of right. The right, the good, is true; the bad grows out of our ignorance. Since we do not know all there is to know, moreover, the true grows and changes with knowledge. So will the good. Like the Universe, this is a growing, changing response. As our knowledge and understanding of the Natural Law grows, so will our capacity for balanced individual and social adjustment change, develop and succeed. So may the Written Law, man's attempt to understand and control the behavior of himself and others, be based upon a grasp of the conduct of man, the correlate of the functioning of the nervous system, itself a product of the Natural Law.

Chapter II

THE BIOLOGY OF MAN

IF IT IS AGREED that the Universe is a place of law and order, then it follows logically that everything in the Universe must also be an expression of the same regularities, the same necessary relatednesses. In the material world—the non-living, the inorganic—the truth of this seems also self-evident. Many will accept this point of view without too much hedging. But, curiously enough, many find it almost impossible to consider living organic beings as equally obvious examples of the operation of lawful processes. Rather it is held that life, because it seems so utterly different from the non-living, must be a special creation; in the Universe, but not of it; a stranger in a cold, rigid, mechanistic environment. Since man is a living being he, like all life, must be profoundly different from rocks and water, from air and heat. Thus these inherent observable differences must be due to the existence of other factors, manifestly other than those of the material cosmos. Hence the belief in a special creation, creation of observable entities—bacteria, fish, birds and man—the results of unknown forces, unknown and therefore mysterious, supernatural. Man in his vanity believes, furthermore, that since he is so different not only from earth and air, but also from all other life, that he is a special-special creation. To justify this, man has been led to create gods of this and that; gods who, having created the human being, must be propitiated, reverenced, served, if a satisfactory life is to be had. All this has resulted in the equally important conviction that the gods, in order to accomplish their ends, have set up rules and regulations, laws and edicts, supernatural laws that were revealed only to the chosen few. The rest of us were supposed to obey them willy-nilly. Is it any wonder that the result of such conviction has been confusion worse confounded? From the very beginning, the language of the gods had to be translated into the vernacular by the sooth-sayers, witches, priests and the fortune tellers. How many of these were the true statements of whatever gods were recognized, or the fevered imaginations of power-hungry men, has never been determined.

The results of all this are abundantly clear. The Universe is no longer One but Two—the material and the living—no longer a unified whole, but rather a cold mechanism in one minuscule corner of which a second contradictory set of beings has been created to confound and debase the material.

To make this possible man, again in his vanity, has had to invent a soul, a spirit, an extraphysical something which could receive the revealed words of the gods and thus control the destiny of the individual. Nearly always the so-called revelations have been used to control others, to require them to do what the prophet says is "right." All this, of course, is the origin of the "ought" in human society, the basis of ethics. Unfortunately, the only way we know it is "right" is because the prophet says so. It assumes that a particular individual has a private pipe-line to the gods and is, therefore, privileged to lay down the Moral Law. Modern Christianity is an example of this. Out of primitive minds, certain persons have abrogated to themselves private knowledge of a Creator, of GOD from whom they receive specific instructions as to how human beings ought to behave.

But is all this really true? Is this the answer to the age-old question of human behavior, to the problem of human relations? If so, then we must abandon the assumption that the Universe is an integrated unit. We must fall back on the concept of a mechanistic, coldly law-abiding material Universe inhabited by specially created living beings. It is argued that if God created matter which obeys certain laws, why could He not create other forms of matter which, in part, at least, obey other kinds of laws —moral, spiritual, Divine Laws? If it be assumed that the Universe had a creator, then certainly this could be true.

But is it? The only evidence which supports the argument comes from the minds of men peering through a glass darkly, limited by a particular cultural background and warped by prejudices which arise in part from personal experience. Can this kind of evidence be trusted? The mind of man is a strange thing with enormous potentials, but it has not always been correct in the pronouncements that flowed from it. Man once thought the earth which he inhabited was the center of the Universe, the core of all that he could see. The earth was flat and the heavens a blue dome covering everything. Matter was made of earth and water, of air and fire. The brain was a hollow chamber filled with a fluid which was an emanation of the soul. These and countless other mistaken ideas make it necessary to examine with extreme care *all* products of the activity of the mind of man.

If we do this, some rather interesting results will follow. It is recognized, of course, that there is no absolute certainty to any alternative ideas. Science, successful as it has been in revolutionizing the environment in which we live, nevertheless can offer no final, complete statement of final truth. As we know more, so does our concept of the good, the true and the beautiful change. Hopefully, with each change, we draw nearer to a final answer. Fortunately, we are still far from it, for life would be uninteresting in the extreme if all problems were solved, if we had nothing toward which to strive, or no problem to unravel.

It should be obvious that this whole question stems from the fact that we have not come to grips with the nature of Man or the meaning of existence. We have taken the unverified "revelations" of a very few minds and tried to enforce them on all the rest of mankind. It behooves us to ask if there is not some way out of the dilemma, some way by which we can find some universals, some factors, operating in all living things everywhere—in London, New York and Peking. Science has discovered many such universals—gravitation, electricity, chemical formulae and reactions, the laws of movement of the heavenly bodies. Using them, man has been able to predict with great certainty the coming of an eclipse, the results of mixing certain chemicals, the trajectory of a missile and of its ultimate fate in space. If Science, aided by technology, can do this, might it not be that the application of the methods of science to the study of mankind would yield equally valid and useful consequence?

To do this we must, perforce, start with Man. Nearly everyone will agree that he is a biological organism, a living thing. As such, he must be made up of the same stuff of life as all other living things. He must be subject to the same laws, the same forces as fish and birds and mice. What is this "stuff" of life? We have reason to believe that we know some things about it. It is called protoplasm, a somewhat jelly-like substance that is found wherever there is life. Essentially, it is made up of four simple chemicals—oxygen, nitrogen, carbon and hydrogen. To be sure, there are probably minute traces of other elements, but the important point is that these constituents are to be found widespread in the non-living world. They are not some special kinds of chemicals; they are exactly like those in earth and sky and sea. What, then, differentiates the living from the dead? The elements in a living organism are bound together by a set of necessary relatednesses, a set of forces which hold the elements in specific patterns, in certain organizations, in unique designs. The complexity of these arrangements is enormous and we have barely made a beginning at unravelling them. We do know, nevertheless, that not only are the elements related to each other by definable forces, but so also are the forces themselves held in bondage by equally important relationships. As a result, the living being exhibits an integrated wholeness, with all elements, all forces linked and chained together to form a whole—a unique unit. In other words, a living organism, a man, is a microcosm, a patterned arrangement of describable entities. It is "micro" because of the microscopic or submicroscopic character of its components. It is like the Cosmos, the Universe, because the same entities and the same patterning forces are found in both.

Given a basic substance—protoplasm—patterned by the organizing forces of the Universe, certain new properties or characteristics arise as a result of the complexity of the necessary relatednesses of the relatively simple component. As always, whether we deal with the non-living or the living, new functions appear as a result of new and increasingly complex interrelationships between the entities. Interestingly enough, the new properties can never be predicted from a knowledge of the constituent elements. By the very nature of the complexities, new attributes appear; new, because although the components are still simple, the inter-relationships are not. In fact, they become so very complex that only a little is known about them. Nature is a far better chemist than is man. She builds unbelievably intricate molecules out of the simplest building blocks. Thus, the very intricacies endow protoplasm with hitherto unknown behavior. It has been said of living things that they exhibit an integrated wholeness not usually recognized in the material universe. It is widely held, moreover, that a living system is always something more than the sum of its parts. Both of these statements contain some truth, but they tend to ignore the fact that the reason why there is merit in them derives from the new attributes which follow from the new relationships, new relationships that result in the formation of new and incredibly varied "organic" molecules. Thus it can be seen that it is the law-enforced new relationships which really separate the living from the non-living. It must be reiterated that the term "law-enforced new relationships" is valid because, were this not so, chaos would characterize life as well as the Universe.

The unity of a living being, be it a slime mold or man, is the result again of a law-enforced compatibility of the activities of the organic molecules of protoplasm. In general, it is these activities which are said to be unique to the living world—unique, perhaps, not in themselves but in the way each is related to all the others.

The first of these properties of protoplasm is usually called "irritability," not in the human sense of fractiousness, but rather in the sense that the ground substance of life will do something, i.e., "react" when it is touched, i.e., "stimulated." The "touch" may be any one or many of the possible *changes* in the environment. It has to be a change, apparently, because protoplasm tends to reach some kind of a near balance to a static external world. Thus, any change in temperature or pressure, any alteration in the chemical or radiation characteristics of the surroundings, results in an adaptation of the organism to the new situation. This adaptation begins at the boundary between the living thing and its surrounding. The boundary, of course, is the cell wall, the place where protoplasm ends and the outside world begins. This is a phase boundary, an area where two physically and chemically different states of matter exist side-by-side. Perhaps right here is the first riddle of life, for a "touch," a "stimulus," somehow gets through the cell wall, the phase boundary, into the stuff of life itself. As a result, the cell wall is sometimes called a semi-permeable membrane, for some, not all the changes, traverse the barrier. In primitive protoplasm, there seems to be no specific portal of entry for any particular stimulus, rather the permeability changes from place to place and from time to time. This is not entirely true of more complex beings, as we shall see later on, since very special gateways develop for very special stimuli.

When a stimulus once passes the cell surface, it immediately comes into contact with the complex organic molecules of protoplasm. What results from this contact is not known in detail. All we know is that the results of this contact are not confined to the portal of entry but spread through the protoplasm itself. Again, in simple living things like amoeba, the consequences of a stimulus tend to radiate throughout the whole system, and thus a second enigma appears—the transmission of a stimulus through protoplasm. Often called "a propagated impulse," the exact nature of the process is unknown. It has been likened to the chain of chemical events in the burning of a fuse. It has certain aspects which suggest an electrical event. That it occurs is beyond question, but our ignorance is great. Like the lack of a particular portal of entry in simple protoplasm, is the lack of particular pathways through the protoplasm. Again, in higher or more complex forms, specific routes are elaborated over which incoming bits of information are propagated.

In any event, an incoming stimulus is distributed and quite promptly a "reaction" occurs. The nature of the activity varies widely. Some can be quite readily observed, but others are obscure. Probably the most obvious result of a propagated stimulus is movement. If you touch almost any living thing it moves, usually away. In its simplest form this can be seen in the streaming of the semi-liquid protoplasm. In higher forms the result of a stimulus may be the contraction of a muscle.

But the reaction involves more than this, for it may involve the initiation of a series of complex chemical processes, including the formation of new protoplasm and of new chemicals, to be stored or excreted. Beyond this the reaction may include nothing more than the passing on of the stimulus to the next adjacent cell. This last is seen in the transmission of a neural impulse from one nerve cell to another.

Finally, the cardinal characteristic of a living being is the ability to reproduce itself. This can be accomplished in several ways. The simplest is for a bit of protoplasm to split into two parts, each fragment then taking up an independent existence as a new individual. Common among the simplest forms of life, it is practically unknown in the higher animals and in man. What starts this fission of protoplasm is not quite clear, nor is the mechanism by which it is accomplished. A second kind of reproduction involves the initiation of the division by some external agent—a specific chemical substance or some physical impact on the cell surface. Such a procedure is frequently found among the insects. Probabaly the most common method found among the complex forms of life is sexual reproduction. This involves two different individuals, one a male and the other a female. The male produces minute, active cells capable of traversing some distances. The female, on the other hand, forms considerably larger units, usually spherical, which cannot move of themselves, but must be transported by outside physical agents—fluids or winds. Under suitable conditions, the motile male sperm reaches a female egg and, penetrating its cell surface, initiates the union of the nucleus of each cell. This is followed shortly by cell division and hence cell multiplication, with the resultant formation of the myriads of cells which make up your body and mine.

Thus it can be seen that a living organism is an integrated, coordinated mass of protoplasmic units (cells), each of which can be stimulated by changes in the chemicals and physical environment, can propagate that stimulus throughout its substance, can react to the stimulus by movement or some change in the physical and chemical properties of the cell and, finally, can develop, in certain circumstances, into specialized cells for the purpose of reproduction. It is possible to describe these characteristics of life in fairly simple terms, but the detailed knowledge of how this is brought about is still shrouded in mystery. Life is still a marvel, so different from the non-living that it is not surprising that many look upon life as a very special creation, a complex which, while made up a non-living elements yet, nevertheless, obeys certain laws not found in the rest of the Universe—in the Universe but not of it. Perhaps the most astonishing and wonder-provoking of all the characteristics of a living system is its property of making some kind of sense out of all the manifold stimuli that constantly bombard each cell throughout its continued existence. This aspect of protoplasm involving discrimination between, and selection of, certain stimuli plus the coordination and integration of all such changes, is the least understood and often the most neglected of all of the describable attributes of life. It endows each living system with wholeness, unity, and unique individuality. It makes it possible for each organism to maintain its uniqueness in the face of a constant flux of physical and chemical bombardment from the outside world. No wonder that many believe we are forced to conclude that in life we are dealing with a physico-chemical system which, nevertheless, is controlled throughout its existence by a something — a soul — which sits on the organism and directs in detail all of its processes. Descriptively, this seems to be true, but it does not follow that the soul is a mysterious, a supernatural agent that is added to physics and chemistry, and is not bound by known laws of the material Universe. Because we are ignorant of how integration is accomplished, it is not necessary that we invent supernatural controls. To do this stifles all attempts at understanding, makes it useless to investigate further. If we call on agents which are not amenable to the methods of science, and invoke mysteries that cannot be described, then we live not in a Universe but in a Multiverse with some known factors operating, but with unspecified others that are essentially unknowable.

Man is a biological system, an integrated whole, made of known chemical units but endowed with special attributes arising in part in the uncounted numbers of biological units, the comprising cells; but also in the necessary relatednesses of all the cells. Since the larger living organisms are congeries of protoplasmic units, size alone has imposed a division of labor on the system; certain cells are set aside for specific purposes. Some are supporting cells forming a framework for the softer more sensitive components; others are capable of change of shape, as in muscles. Still others perform the necessary function of converting foodstuffs into available chemical energy. But the activities of all these specialized cells must be related to each other in rigorously controlled fashion, else the organism would fly apart. Hence certain cells possess increased sensitivity to light, to sound, to smell, to taste and, on a somewhat different level, to touch, temperature, pain and pressure. Finally, all these manifold activities must be tied together in the bundle of an integrated wholeness and thus certain cells become the carriers of the bits of information derived from the outside world, putting them all together and transmitting them to specific points. Thus, in man, as elsewhere, in addition to the bony framework, the muscular apparatus, the chemical factories, there is the communication system made up of the brain and its attendant nerve.

All this has been brought about by the differentiation of particular cells for the performance of specific functions. Specialization occurs in the development of the adult individual from the fertilized egg, and equally important in the evolution of life from the earliest slime to modern man.

Chapter III

THE EVOLUTION OF MAN

IN THE RATHER formal and traditional exposition of the nature of protoplasm just given, there are, of course, many details left out. However, certain aspects of protoplasm of peculiar significance to those people interested in a particular living organism — man — must be emphasized. It must not be forgotten that man is just as much a living system made of the essential stuff of life— protoplasm — as birds, and beasts, and bugs. He is the stuff of life itself and, as we have seen, is made up of a relatively limited array of chemical substances combined with each other in extraordinarily complex patterns. The chemical substances are as common as table salt, but in some way, in some as yet unknown fashion, these ordinary substances are linked and chained together into the infinitely complex protoplasm. As we have seen, this protoplasm has certain capacities which arise not out of the chemical substances themselves, but out of the way they are linked and chained together. It is the way in which these simple chemical compounds are related to each other that results in the appearance of new properties, new capacities which are not inherent in any single one of the original substances. Little as we know about the factors which compel the proper combination of these chemical substances, nevertheless, it is clear that the combination endows this new and different kind of thing with unique and exceedingly interesting properties. The properties of irritability, in other words, a capacity to react to changes in the external and internal environment; the ability to transmit throughout its substance bits of information so brought to the living system; the capacity to integrate and coordinate all the stimuli which fall on the surface of the organism, and the remarkable function of doing something about all this information, is unique. It must not be forgotten that these properties come out of the combinations

28

of the substances, not out of the substances alone. This, of course, is the key and the central problem of all biology, the origin of pattern, of form, of the arrangements of parts which makes it possible to identify plants, to differentiate animals one from another, to recognize living systems we see, or when we read an adequate description of a particular organism.

Now perhaps the most exciting thing about a living system of even the most primitive sort, is that it has a basic integrity; it has a unity, a wholeness, a characteristic peculiar to that particular kind of living system. This uniqueness or wholeness of the organism has been said by biologists, over the years, to be something more than the sum of its component parts. The combinations endow the living system with this wholeness and this unique property. The amazing thing is that the living system maintains its wholeness, its characteristic pattern and form in the midst of an incredibly varied flux of physical and chemical changes in the world around it and within the living system itself. This capacity of a living system to make its own substance out of raw materials, to maintain its form in the face of innumerable stimuli, is the miracle of life.

In the very simplest forms of primitive slime, where raw protoplasm without much form exists, the kind of integration of stimuli and reaction to stimuli must necessarily be of a very simple sort. This means that the capacity of the living system to adjust itself to the widely changing environmental circumstances is definitely limited. Unless there is the right kind of environment — a fitness of the environment — protoplasm cannot survive. And yet it is perfectly clear that simple protoplasm has survived. The reason it has survived is this very interesting thing. Early in the history of living things, the factors in the living organism which helped to define its characteristic form, the units which are commonly called the genes, the essential elements of heredity in the protoplasm, are numerous enough so that various combinations are possible. Theoretically, this should mean that there should be many variations in the kind of protoplasm which can result from new combinations of genes. In all probability, however, while the possibilities are numerous, the actual surviving combinations

are relatively limited, because most of the changes produce protoplasm which is no better able to handle the varied environment
than is the original mass of protoplasm itself. Most of these new
combinations, called mutations, do not survive. But some of them
do. And they do this probably in large part because the new combinations endow the protoplasm with new capacities, new ability
to meet changing environmental circumstances.

One of the earliest and outstanding examples of the consequence of these new changes is the appearance of bits of protoplasm which have an increased sensitivity to certain types of
changes in the environment. So, for example, there developed
spots in primitive one-celled animals which were more sensitive
to light than the general protoplasm of the whole organism. This
increased sensitivity to light makes it possible for the living organism to adjust more adequately to its environmental variations.
The light has not brought forth this change in the protoplasm,
for it has never been possible to change the pattern of protoplasm
by voluntarily imposing upon the protoplasm some particular
kind of special stimulus. Rather, in the genetic combinations, with
the control which they exert over the protoplasm as a whole,
certain re-arrangements of chemical substances within the protoplasm itself, result in a lowered threshold or an increased sensitivity to light itself. This is a very important development and,
in one sense of the word, seems to be accidental, because we have
relatively limited control over the re-combination of genes which
produce mutations. We are learning more and more about it all
the time so, under proper conditions, inherited properties of the
living system can be enhanced by mating one living system with
such properties to another of a similar sort. This is the technique
of most animal breeders. But since in the primitive protoplasm
there can be no selection of the proper combinations, it is largely
a matter of accident what particular combination of genetic characters will be formed; and even more largely a matter of chance,
if such re-combined patterns of organization find themselves in
an environment in which they can continue to survive.

If, then, a living system appears with a bit of protoplasm
which is more sensitive to light than general protoplasm, this is

of no use to the organism unless it can be built into the integrating systems of the whole organism and appropriately distributed to mechanisms through which the protoplasm reacts to its environment. In general, the information brought in by the light-sensitive protoplasm or, perhaps better, picked up by the light-sensitive protoplasm, must be transmitted to the whole organism through characteristic channels. This means that there must be formed within the protoplasm itself pathways more readily travelled by the light stimuli than is to be found in the general protoplasm. The transmitted stimulus of light then can be spread more rapidly through the proper channels in the protoplasm and bring about an appropriate response. In primitive systems this appropriate response is of a very simple sort. It is a *yes* or *no* proposition. It results in orientation in the living system to the light source probably because by orientation better food stuffs become available or, in certain other forms, it may result in the avoidance of light by the living system because the kind of materials it needs for its own constitution is to be found in dark places. This is like the *on-off* proposition of electronic computers.

There are only two things this simple protoplasm can do, move toward or move away from the source of the stimulus. It is obvious that if we have more efficient protoplasm, better integration of the efficiencies, and prompter transport of the integrations through the substance of the protoplasm, the organism becomes better able to survive the vagaries of the changing environment. We know from the history of the earth that the physical environment of the earth has changed remarkably over the eons of time and only living systems with genuine competence to react to the changing systems successfully could continue to live.

It must be obvious that another characteristic must sooner or later appear to improve the competence of the organism to continue to live and that is the development of better methods of movement. It is not surprising, therefore, that we find that some kinds of protoplasm, whose patterns are undeniably under genetic control, so designed and organized that they can change their shape. Now interestingly enough, this change in shape is like the early response of the whole organism. The shape of the organism changes through extension or contraction. Such protoplasm is obviously the forerunner of the things we call muscles. But do not forget that all through this whole complicated story, the individual integrity of the organism maintains itself in the face of all these vagaries. The coordination of all the stimuli which fall on the most primitive protoplasm results in a phenomenal ability of protoplasm to receive, discriminate, and coordinate all this incoming information and to bring about an appropriate response that has survival value. Now all these properties of primitive protoplasm endow that particular living system with behavior, a behavior which is the direct consequence of the design and arrangement of parts of the protoplasm itself, in other words, the result of the linking and chaining together of relatively simple chemical substances. Just how a living system can build so many complex chemical substances out of these primitive substances, no one really knows, but it is perfectly clear that protoplasm is a far better chemist than any of the chemical factories in the land.

Now one would think that having a mass of material substance, of living stuff or protoplasm, which has a very considerable capacity to adjust to changes in the environment at a somewhat higher level than elemental slime, that this might have been the end of the road, but it is clear that this is not so. Nature, apparently not satisfied with the achievements in the first step of making bigger and better living systems, has gone on to greater refinement of all these properties; greater sensitivity, greater speed of transmission, greater capacity for differentiation and organization, greater capacity for movement. This is not the time nor the place to detail in rigorous fashion the various stages through which this refinement of living systems has taken place, but there are some stages in it which warrant a word of description. When the living system was a single cell organism, and that alone, with all of its properties confined within the cell wall of a single cell organism, the kind of behavior determined by the pattern of organization of protoplasm was necessarily fairly simple. But Nature was apparently looking for better capacity to adjust to the environment and so she set about refining the protoplasm beyond that to be found in a single cell. This was accomplished by setting aside certain cells for certain specific purposes and then joining these varieties of cells into colonies. There are many colonial living systems which have unique cells in the colony with special jobs to do. There are cells which are primarily set aside for purposes of reproduction; there are other cells which are set aside to be more sensitive to physical and chemical changes in the environment; and still other cells which serve the purpose of transmitting all the information brought into the colony with greater speed and efficiency throughout the whole system. Curiously enough, in these early colonial forms there does not seem to be any specific group of cells which are concerned with integration, the coordination of all the stimuli, and yet these colonial forms retain their integrity, their characteristic form and functions apparently without a special integrating, coordinating organ or specially designed cells. In some unknown fashion, all the information received seems to be spread through the whole colony of cells which are all adjusted to each other in such a way that the organism continues to exist and to behave in a typical and normal fashion. This setting aside of special cells in multicellular organisms for specific jobs, reaches its first stage in greater efficiency, of course, when the more highly differentiated cellular components are grouped and chained together in a system, an organ system. This occurs when these specially devised cells wander from their point of origin in the many celled organism and are gathered together into specific areas. This gathering together of special cells with special abilities is the basis for the formation and appearance of the nervous system, which in the early forms is quite simple. Many nerve cells, as they are now called, with, however, not too many interconnections, are all grouped together into a particular part of the living organism. So we find simple living systems like insects, or worms, with well-defined collections of specialized cells grouped in a recognizable nervous system. Interestingly enough, when this conglomeration of specialized units, the nerve cells, appear, a still more refined kind of specialized cell joins the nervous system apparently with the major job on its hands of integrating and coordinating all the information that comes into the living system. Again, this is an example of

Nature's successful integration of incoming information in the single celled animal and adding to that capacity by means of the appearance of specialized cells in a nervous system. So we find through the wandering of cells from their point of origin, the formation of a nervous system which is more sensitive to the changes in the physical and chemical environment, better able to integrate all forms of information, transmitting such information to the appropriate destination more rapidly than was hitherto possible; and through the clever manipulation of relaxing and contracting muscle tissue on the mechanical framework of bones, increasing enormously the kinds of movement which the organism can perform. All this leads quite clearly into the development of the living organism — man — who has all the properties of all living systems plus the very extraordinary uniqueness and individuality of his behavior pattern. His behavior is the consequence of the way the primitive elements are linked and chained together to form protoplasmic mechanisms which are built into the organ system we know as the nervous system. With the appearance of nerves, every living thing exhibits more and more varied ways of behaving, and acquires as a consequence, more uniqueness, more individuality. The appearance during evolutionary time of more efficient sensing systems, more rapid techniques of communication, better coordinating and integrating centers has resulted in our time in uniquely individual beings — man. In a very real sense, man is a nervous system, unbelievably complex, different from every other identifiable object that we know of in the Universe. Because of the billions of nerve cells built into the human body, the variety of behavior patterns characteristic of humans is very great. It is so manifold that many have concluded that behavior is environmentally determined. As we shall see, there is enough truth in this point of view to add confusion to an already extremely complicated problem. To many, man is a mass of putty that can be molded nearer to the heart's desire by taking thought thereto. Given an amorphous handful of protoplasm and the right kind of an environment, a constant stream of suitably chosen stimuli, any infant can be trained to be a Beethoven, an Einstein, or a Hitler. This is the central, primary assumption lying behind a great deal of thinking of educationists, religionists and professional do-gooders. It is a conviction which is almost never dragged out into the open. If it were, the logical consequences of the theory would be so at variance with experience that its falseness would be immediately apparent.

On the contrary, in spite of the bombardment of human beings by an infinitude of bits of information through eye, ear, touch and so on, each one of us has definite limitations which cannot be gainsaid no matter what is done to us. On the other hand, because of the seemingly unlimited permutations and combinations of the individual nerve cells, the potentialities of man seem to be almost without limit. Hence man has invented the doctrine of free will, the dualistic notion of a mind or spirit. He has an ego, a soul, something that sits on but not in his body, a supernatural something that is over and above the material universe, subject to peculiar laws that cannot be unravelled by the experimental technique of science. Unfortunately, the verifiable facts in the matter lend considerable weight to this point of view. Hence we are driven to the conclusion that facts are subject to different interpretations and that it is eminently worthwhile to consider a very different approach to the problems arising from our presence in this unbelievably complex Universe and on this confusing and bewildering corner we call the world.

Chapter IV

MAN AS AN ORGANISM

F ROM what has been presented here, it should be obvious that as a result of the selection through survival of certain kinds of protoplasmic systems, there has developed a particular kind of system which we know as man. He exists because with more efficient machinery he can more successfully adapt to the manifold and extremely varied bits of information derived from the manifold world about him. He can do this because he is a nervous system, exceedingly sensitive, superbly organized, so that he can adjust adequately by means of a great variety of activities. But in order to make this possible the nervous system, since it is made up of protoplasmic units, the nerve cells, must be constantly provided with food stuffs from which it gets the energy to cooperate. To make this possible, the organization of man, as in all living systems consists, in addition to the nervous system, of chemical factories capable of changing the raw material which makes up the physical and chemical environment into the particular compounds necessary to the continued activity of the nerve cells. But all nerve cells, though made of basic protoplasm, are not alike in the kinds of food they need. Hence we find many kinds of chemical factories capable of providing the material out of which a nerve cell, along with all the other cells of the body, can re-build its own protoplasm as its energy sources are diminished during activity, and also to manufacture and release into the blood stream many very complex chemicals, most commonly called hormones. It has been said by some that it is these hormones which determine behavior, for it seems to be reasonably clear that under certain conditions a change in the hormonal components of the circulation blood can produce what seem to be the changes in behavior. But it can be seen without much difficulty that it is a false assumption. The hormones are chemical substances which are necessary for the operation of certain groups of neurones. Without these chemical stuffs, the neurones cannot operate at their normal efficiency. When provided, therefore, these neurones can take part in the control of activity and it is the control which these neurones exert which determines the behavior, not the hormone. The hormone, in other words, is nothing more than the gas that makes the automobile go, but it does not determine the difference between a Ford or a Rolls Royce; that is a pattern of the functioning of the neurones which make up the central and peripheral nervous system. Now we have seen that this patterning, this necessary relatedness, between the component parts of which all biological systems are built, is not a happenstance, accidental nor chaotic phenomenon, but is the result of the operation of rigorously imposed natural law. We know something about the natural law that is involved in this but, unfortunately, only a very small fraction of it. Every aspect of the living process, from the simplest to the most complex, requires energy. This energy must come in from the outside, must be organized and, what is perhaps the most important of all, directed in certain channels. Just as railroads and trucks are necessary to distribute the food stuffs which are raised on the farmlands of the country and have to be directed over certain routes to certain destinations, destinations where this foodstuff can be most effectively utilized, so in the living system the great mass of energy absorbed in foodstuffs has to be channeled, programed, directed through certain areas and to certain destinations in the living system. It is currently fashionable to look upon all aspects of biological systems as basically chemical, just as nearly all the activities of our modern understanding of physics is basically electrical. The probability is that both of these are of vital importance in our understanding of the living as well as the nonliving universe. But just as our own social organization is not completely chaotic, but is organized, so in the living system all these required behaviors of the living thing have to be significantly controlled and regulated in order that the system can continue to exist. This is a basic requirement of life. Unfortunately overlooked in living systems is this; that all that goes on in the living system is a directed process. If this were not so, it would not be possible for a living system to maintain its continued existence for a fraction of a millisecond. Moreover, all of these activities which have chemical aspects are nearly always contact influences; one chemical substance is related by contact to another chemical substance and, as a consequence, a third kind of chemical substance develops. The extraordinary thing about a living system is that out of relatively simple components it builds incredibly complex organic compounds. We have only a glimmering of an idea of just how this is brought about. But the fact that contact forces of a chemical nature are important does not preclude another very interesting aspect of life, and that is, that somehow the living system has characteristics which differentiate it from other collections of simple chemical compounds. This, as we have seen, is the wholeness of the living system, the unique organismic character, the thing that makes it possible for us to recognize one kind of living system from another, not only by its component parts, but by the way it acts. This gives to the living system a wholeness, a series of properties which are known by biologists to be greater than the accumulation of the component parts. There is always something more than just the addition of the chemical factors to be found in the living system.

It is not surprising, once this is recognized, that mankind over the years has invented all kinds of terms to describe something more than the sum of the component parts. Man has endowed himself with a soul, with a mind, or spirit to explain this over-all wholeness. But where can this wholeness come from? It quite clearly cannot come just from the addition of chemicals to the substance of protoplasm. It cannot come just from the contact forces which relate one chemical substance to another, because it is clear from a great many experiments that the fate of individual cells in the growing organism is not only a function of the neighboring cells, which would be true of a truly chemical phenomenon, but it is also a function of the place which those cells occupy in the whole organism. Thus it has been shown in proper stages of development that groups of cells taken from a head end of an embryo and transplanted into the tail end of an embryo lose their head characters and become tail cells. This is because they have been transplanted from an area at one end of the organism to a different area at the other end and have assumed the properties of the area to which they have been transplanted. This situation is true, however, for a limited period of time only for, before very long, head cells become so firmly determined as head cells that they retain their characters even when transplanted to distant regions. This cannot be explained by appeal to contact chemical forces. There can be only one explanation and that is that there are distance forces operating in the living system, forces of sufficient precision and magnitude to control with great precision the growth and development of particular cells in particular regions, so that eye cells are always eye cells, after a certain stage of development, no matter what happens to them. To repeat, then, this is an organismic factor, a wholeness of the organism which, in a very real sense of the word, controls the whole activity of the organism.

It has been suggested above that the control of behavior is the function of the nervous system. That is true at the time when the growing system acquires specific functions. In other words, when the embryo develops organs. It is not true, apparently, before this time. We cannot, therefore, invoke the nervous system as the directing force in the very young dividing cells of an early embryo. There must be some other factor involved that starts off this directed growth and development. It seems reasonably clear that if this is to be accomplished it has to result from the presence of directional forces or, in technical terms, vector forces which give direction to any process. Nearly all chemical forces are not directional, they have no vector properties. To be sure, there are some chemical processes which do seem to have direction within very limited areas but it is clear, equally, that chemical directive forces operate only within the limits of a given cell and can hardly be expected to control such phenomena as the development of head cells or tail cells. It should be clear, then, that the answer to the problem of patterning of the protoplasmic systems of every living organism is not likely to be solved on the basis of chemistry alone. Some other factors must be invoked. Curiously enough, biologists, over the years, have not been much interested in the electrical aspects of living systems, this in spite of the fact that heart waves, brain waves and nerve currents have been known for a long while, but have usually been considered to be nothing more nor less than the consequence of protoplasmic activity.

The movements of the heart, the firing of neurones in the nervous system, and so on, have been shown to be associated with recordable electrical phenomena. To be sure, we do not know what electricity is. (As a distinguished scientist has said, "Electricity is the way Nature behaves.") We know that the important factors in the physical non-living universe are a product of the activity of electric forces. These electrical forces have vector properties, unlike contact forces of chemistry. They operate over distances, they demand a flow of electrons from one point to another and, in the process, set up electrical fields. It matters not whether these are called electrodynamic, electromagnetic, or inductive fields; they are electrical fields. It has been shown without much doubt that these exist in living systems and since such fields have the power to determine the direction of the flow of energy and the movement of all charged particles which come within the range of the field, it would seem reasonably safe to assume that electrical fields provide the necessary factor to explain the existence of an organismic whole.

The very complex living system has its characters, both structural and functional, determined by the presence of this electrical field. It is not surprising, of course, that people should ask at once, Whence comes this field, or this electricity? Where are the generators, or the batteries which provide the potential differences which set up the current flow within every system? Well, it is doubtful if there are any actual generators, as such. There are no motors or dynamos or batteries in a strict sense to be recognized in living systems. But it is well-known in the physical universe that wherever there is a difference between two states of nature, there exists at the boundaries between them a thing known as a phase boundary. Because the two stages of nature are different on opposite sides of this boundary, the charged components of both states are different, otherwise, they would not be different states. In other words, the phase boundary marks the area where charges of different sign are separated from each other and as soon as there is a difference in charge, or the accumulation of charged particles on one side of the phase boundary which is different from the other, a potential gradient is set up which then determines the direction in which the flow of electrons or of energy will occur. Thus, there is set across this phase boundary an electrical field. The accumulation of all these electrical fields, (there must be billions of them in every living system), provide enough separation of charges to produce rather extraordinary differences in potential. These can be measured, polarities established, and field factors recorded. It has been shown, for example, that in any conducting medium, a living system such as an aquatic animal, is surrounded by a field which can be detected outside the body of the organism up to a distance of almost a millimeter. Potential gradients or voltage differences, under experimental conditions, have been reported, when the contacts made for the recording instruments are not on the animal itself, but within close proximity to it in the surrounding medium. It is possible to show, furthermore, that again under proper experimental conditions the passage of a nerve impulse down a nerve trunk, can be picked up in the air surrounding the nerve. Such things would not be possible if electrical fields were not present in living systems. Hence it would seem reasonable to assume, as a working hypothesis, that an organismic system, a living organism, is made up not only of chemical stuffs but of electrical fields capable of controlling and determining the position and movement of all charged particles within the system.

One of the very interesting aspects of development is the fact that the one constant in development is this organismic, wholeness factor. This has been known since the days of Aristotle, as a set of controlling factors which determine that the acorn will grow into the oak tree and not into a fig tree. It is the one constant. It would seem reasonable, therefore, to assume that a field possesses this constancy, this characteristic of directing the growth and development of every living system. Now one of the consequences of this, of course, is the appearance of different organs in the living system and particularly in the appearance of the nervous system. Although biological activity, whatever its nature, exhibits electrical aspects, the nervous system seems to be the system with the most clear-cut electrical properties. While there are some who maintain that the propagation of the nervous impulse down the nerve fiber is basically chemical, there is plenty of evidence to indicate that electrical phenomena play a very important part in it, so much so that every conducting nerve shows, when it is active, the presence of an action current potential difference. These electrical properties of the nervous system are so extraordinary that it is possible to pick up so-called brain waves not in contact with the brain, but with the scalp. These waves must traverse skin and bone and the coverings of the brain, to say nothing of the fluid surrounding the brain. In spite of these obstacles, the inductive fields which are a correlate of neural activity create disturbances which can be picked up at a considerable distance from their source. If such fields can be detected by instruments, it is not at all surprising that the far more sensitive protoplasmic systems which make up the other cells of the body could also be influenced by inductive fields. There is great probability, therefore, that all the organ systems, the fate of all the cells which compose them and their arrangement and their eventual functional activity, should be the consequence of the existence of such fields. This, of course, will be severely questioned by those who maintain that the structure of any living system is the consequence of the activities of minute components of the nucleus of the cell, the so-called genes. These have been identified in some forms and their position in the nucleus regularized and shown to be correlated with the appearance of specified physical agents, the units within the cell which determine what its make-up is and will be, and what part it will play in growth and development. While in recent years a certain amount of evidence has been accumulating to show that certain enzymes may be responsible for some of the aspects of this inherited control there is, as yet, no solid theory of how the genes control development and heredity. Presumably genes control your stature, the color of your hair, and so on, but how they do this is yet to be discovered. It would not seem to be stretching the argument too far to suggest that the inductive fields, which result from potential differences and the flow of electrons in the living system, are the primary factors which control the activities not only of the whole cell, but of all of its component parts, including the genes. Furthermore, the electrical properties of the genes themselves which, of course, have never been measured but which, almost certainly are present may, through inductive fields exert control over growth and development. It must be emphasized again that all living systems exhibit this organic wholeness and the one measurable property of the whole organism which can be determined with accuracy and certainty is an electrical field. Such a field is primary, *the* essential, basic characteristic of all livings systems in general, and of man in particular. It should be clear that the idea of such a field is not some mysterious hypothesis dragged in from the outside, but is a measurable property of the living and non-living universe. For our understanding, such a field is dependent upon the nature of the entities, the charged particles, which are to be found within the field. The field does not exist independently of the units, the chemical substances, the atoms within the living system. It is quite definitely dependent upon them, for their presence makes possible the existence of the field and the field determines, through the component parts, the necessary relatednesses, the necessary structural properties, the necessary form. It cannot be emphasized too strongly that the presence of such a field is a primary requirement of our understanding of the nature of man and of the universe. Moreover, fields, as such, can never act independently of other fields. Any local disturbance in a field must be propagated to other fields. So in the living system, a field such as is to be found in any particular part of the organism must necessarily be a component part of the organismic field of the entire organism. These fields are primary. They can be measured, they can be identified with accuracy and, perhaps what is more important than anything else, they have predictive value.

Since fields are basic primary properties of all living systems, they must be present in man. In man they determine, through the agent of the component common chemicals, a particular pattern and form upon which rests all the activity of the organism. This activity, of course, is what we commonly think of when we use the term, "behavior." We do not know anything about a living system except by the way it behaves. It is also clear that the field-induced structures exist first and functional activity follows. Now since we are primarily interested in the nature of man, it would seem a satisfactory answer to the wholeness of man that he be looked upon as a collection of simple chemical salts or substances organized and patterned in particular ways; so patterned that he exhibits quite clearly the presence of purpose in the design of the system, the end result of which, at least so far as our present stage in evolution goes, is the appearance of the unique, complete-ly individual — man. But just as fields cannot exist autonomously and independent of each other, so living systems are dependent upon not only their physical environment, their chemical environ-ment, but also their human environment. This, then, brings us to the next stage in our inquiry into the nature of the particular organ system in man whose activity exhibits the presence of fields and which, in the last analysis, determines completely the behavior of man. It must not be forgotten, of course, that every living system demands chemical substances for its continued existence. These are of vital importance. Just as you cannot run an auto-mobile without gas, so biological systems cannot exist without food. But all the food in the world, no matter how carefully selected, cannot change in any significant fashion the structure of the human being or its consequent activity. It can enable the structure to continue its existence, it can provide the structure with the necessary energy for its operation, but it can never put into the organism behavior which is not there to start with. The only thing the chemical environment can do, so far as anybody knows, is either to provide the energy required by its functional activity, or to damage some part of its responding system. Chem-istry creates nothing new in a living system. It is not now possible to make a silk purse out of a sow's ear, any more than it was two thousand years ago. It behooves us, therefore, to turn now to a discussion of how the nervous system controls this activity which we know only through the general term of "behavior."

Chapter V

MAN IS HIS NERVOUS SYSTEM

We have seen that man, like every other living system, is made up of the raw stuff of life — protoplasm. This consists of complex combinations of relatively common chemicals. The variety of the inter-relationships between these chemicals endows the protoplasm with many new abilities. We have seen further that over the long ages of evolution this protoplasmic basic stuff has undergone many changes. Most of these have been such as to add efficiency to the capacity of living protoplasm to adjust to its manifold environment. In the course of this, there has been built up in protoplasmic mechanisms, cells with specialized functions. So we see that certain of the cells provide the necessary skeletal framework of all vertebrates. Other cells, modified in a different way, form muscles to enable the organisms to move with greater variety and facility and with greater effectiveness. We have seen that foodstuffs brought into the living system through the digestive tract, which is another set of specialized cells, have to be transported throughout the living system by a very effective delivery system — the blood stream. This blood stream carries food to all parts of the living organism, providing the necessary energy for all the activities of the component parts. Furthermore, there has appeared a respiratory system, a breathing system which, through the lungs, is able to take in oxygen from the inspired air in quantities large enough to provide the basic requirement for the conversion of the raw foodstuffs of the digestive system into highly specialized organic compounds which are necessary for the activities of the other biological systems.

This introduces a very considerable complexity into the living system, a complexity which apparently reaches its maximum in the organism we now know as man. We do not know, of course, that man is the end of this long evolutionary process, but he is top of the pattern so far as our present knowledge goes. These various organ systems, however, do not act autonomously. They all have to be regulated, coordinated, tied together in a significant fashion so that they can all work together in harmony for the continued good of that particular protoplasmic system. All the activities of these subsidiary organ systems — the skeleton, the muscles, the digestive system, the respiratory system, the blood stream — all have to be coordinated to produce an effective and efficient piece of machinery. It cannot, I think, be argued that this incredibly complex system has appeared as a result of chance. It is a designed system without which none of us could last for any period of time.

The mechanism above all which makes it possible for this multitudinous and varied group of cells to work together in internal harmony, is the nervous system. We all know that we have brains; we all know that we have a spinal cord; we all know that we have nerves stretching from the central nervous system to the various parts of the body, thus controlling the chemical functions of the digestive system, the endocrine system, and the movements of the muscles which make possible the activity of the organism in response to the internal and external environment. We know only about each other, or about ourselves, by acticvity, by man's behavior; and this behavior, without question, is completely determined by the functions and activities of the nervous system. It seems to be quite clear, however, that all nerve cells do not require the same kind of chemical foodstuffs. Certain nuclear masses, as they are called, or collections of nerve cells, require a particular kind of chemical. A neighboring collection of cells requires a different kind. It can be argued cogently, therefore, that under certain conditions, the right kind of chemistry can provide maximum output from a given group of neurones and this seems, from the external observer's point of view, to change the behavior of the organism. In a certain sense, this is true; but it is not completely true because the chemistry does not put anything into this nervous system that was not there before. It simply enables any particular part, or the whole nervous system, to operate at its maximum efficiency. Now because of the incredible complexity of the nervous system, it always looks as though behavior were a modifiable thing. It is modifiable, within limits, but so far as we know, we cannot put into the nervous system anything that was not there beforehand. We can, however, through a great variety of media, enable the nervous system to operate all of its components with maximum efficiency.

Since this nervous system controls behavior, it is interesting to note that there are at least four different kinds of behavior which can be, within certain limits, quite sharply differentiated from each other and yet remain a part of the wholeness of the organism. The first and simplest control of behavior is what we call reflex behavior. By this, we simply mean that any given stimulus, any given change in the physical or chemical environment, may produce a local and quite prompt, rapid response to the stimulus. This is quite automatic; we have almost no control over it; it is the living organism's — man's — defense against inimical factors in his environment and his first method of adequately controlling the quick response of the muscular system to any change in either the external or the internal environment. You all know that in man, when the knee is tapped sharply, there follows promptly a funny kick to his foot, known as a knee jerk. This kick is simply a reflex contraction of one set of muscles and the relaxation of another, and is carried out within given regions of the spinal cord in quite an automatic behavior. There are many such reflexes throughout the body.

On top of this, there is a second level of the control of behavior, an automatic synthesis of reflexes. This is sometimes known as non-modifiable, automatic, or instinctive behavior. It is the kind of behavior pattern which involves coordination of wide groups of reflexes into prompt and smooth movement. It is controlled, in part, by the cerebellum — the little brain — and in part by groups of neurones deep in the heart of the nervous system, sometimes known as the basal ganglia. Most of these automatic behavior patterns are inherited. They are inherited from our evolutionary ancestors and they are inherited from our immediate ancestors. A typical example of this automatic inherited behavior pattern is the difference between trotters and pacers in horses; the difference in the kind of behavior that a cat exhibits when walking and running, from that of a dog under the same conditions. It is the kind of thing we notice when we watch the human gait — the right arm swings alternately with the left leg. This is a balanced control of behavior which is not learned, that is built into the nervous system and, on the whole, is not very often subject to much modification.

A more complex form of this automatic behavior is to be found in what we call, rather loosely, the movements called forth by emotions. It is only through such motor activity that we can recognize appetite, love, fear, rage, not only in ourselves, but in all men whether they be black, yellow, or white. Such expressions of instincts and emotions form a great part of our human inheritance. The automatic nesting habits of birds, the mating habits of animals of all kinds, the very complex behavior patterns of courtship are all of this sort — inherited patterns of behavior. It is held by many, of course, that the expressions of the face are of this automatic sort. When we look at someone else we think, most of the time, that we can tell whether he is angry, or fearful, or affectionate, or cheerful. These are automatic controls of the muscles of the face which result in patterns of behavior which can be classified. Needless to say, this is not so easy as it appears. Many of the facial expressions which one uses are not different enough from each other to make it possible for us to say that this particular individual is angry, or cheerful, but apparently there are many other items in the behavior, movements of the rest of the body, which reinforce the expressions of the face. It must be emphasized that these automatic integrations of reflex activity are inherited; they are non-modifiable; they go on all the time at a level which is below ordinary awareness. The particular bits of information which initiate these coordinated, automatic behavior patterns find certain arrangements of neurones in the central nervous system which are fixed. They are part of our heritage and, in many ways, they define the fundamental differences which exist between kinds of animals and, in man, between different individuals.

Finally, to this reflex control and automatic control is added the most extraordinary development of the whole long history of evolution. Superimposed on top of these in-born controlling mechanisms is the thing which, in common parlance, is called the brain. This is a part of the nervous system which has undergone enormous enlargement during evolution. It is of importance to us because it adds a whole new range of controls of behavior. Man likes to think that this brain, as it is called, endows him with a number of behavior patterns which make him different from other animals. He believes that, as a result of this, he has freedom of choice, the capacity to make judgments, the ability to discriminate between a great variety of sensory inputs. Hand-in-hand with the appearance of real brains — gray matter, cortex — appear particular groups of neurones with increased sensitivity to specific compoents of the environment. Eyes, ears, smell and taste, and many of the simpler forms of sensation — touch and temperature, pain and pressure — are also elaborated.

It is now believed that the gray matter of the brain is made up of some ten billion cells linked and chained together in complex patterns. As a result, man is said to possess intelligence. This is simply a term to describe the ability of the cortex to take a great mass of information derived from all of its special senses, all parts of its body (including the vascular system, the respiratory system and the digestive system and the sex glands) and in some quite mysterious manner, put all these bits of information together and come out with a characteristic response. This characteristic response is the thing we know as behavior. It is the thing we know in another sense, also, as the personality of the individual. The reaction pattern, in other words, the simple, ordinary behavior, is the only way we know enough about each other to define characteristic personalities. Thus the nervous system is man. You and I are what we are because of these ten billion cells of our nervous systems. We are what we are because these ten billion cells are linked and chained together into characteristic patterns whose activity results in what we know as behavior.

It now seems quite clear from all the information which we possess that these cells in the gray matter of the cortex, these cellular components of the brain, are so arranged that in many ways they behave like computing systems. As a matter of fact, this really should be reversed. Computing systems are arranged because they can be so designed as to show results which are not too unlike the kind of reaction systems which the nervous systems possess. In fact, knowledge of the nervous system has been a major factor in the development of all kinds of computers. It is perfectly clear that a computer operates because certain kinds of information are fed into it in characteristic patterns and ways. The information is programmed to suit the particular computer. The information which is fed into the computing mechanism of the nervous system is so enormously varied that we really do not know how to program the information coming into our particular type of nervous system computer. The man-made machine cannot operate with just any kind of information. If all kinds of great varieties of information are fed into computers, out of it comes not an adeqate answer, but confusion worse confounded. On the other hand, man's nervous system can take all kinds of information and, in some completely mysterious fashion, make sense of all this information and, by this process, control and regularize behavior in the normal, human way. The computer has to have a human being program the kind of information which is fed into it; moreover, the computer was designed by human beings, and the old argument that the machines can take over the functions of man is nonsense. While it is dangerous to say that things cannot be done, it would seem highly unlikely that man can ever invent a computer which will duplicate the activities of the human nervous system. Since, moreover, the programming for a computer is prepared by a mind of some human being and, therefore, can decide what is right or what is wrong for that particular computer, so far as we know we have no method of programming the kinds of information that go into the nervous system. Theoretically, this should be the job of education. The only difficulty is that, so far as the computer is concerned, man has learned to know what is right and what is wrong, but so far as the kind of information that goes into the human nervous system is concerned, no one knows what is going to be right or wrong for that particular nervous system. Just to make it more difficult, the kind of information which is right for one nervous system is not necessarily right for another nervous system. This is the reason why human beings scattered over the face of the globe with all kinds of variations in the environment, both physical and ideational, behave so differently. Why is it that behavior of an inhabitant of London, or of New York, which is labeled under the ordinary criteria as being adequate behavior, is totally inadequate to handle a problem of behavior in the East, or some more remote part of the world? It can be argued, of course, that the difference is the kind of education which the groups have received, and, undoubtedly, this is partly true, but this, of course, adds an enormous responsibility to all educational programs. But beside all this, there are two aspects of the functioning of the nerve cells of the brain about which we do know something. One of the consequences of the enormous numbers of neurones involved is the development in the human nervous system of highly critical discriminations. Some of these are visual, some of these are auditory, some of these are smell, some of these are touch and pressure, all of which endow mankind with some rather unique attributes. The artist discriminates color and value to an astonishing degree. This kind of thing is perhaps more obvious in the nervous system of musicians. Auditory discriminations can be of such a sort that the individual can be said to have perfect pitch, but even more than that, he can appreciate musical sounds with much greater sensitivity and effectiveness than many of us. It has been said that animals, such as hounds, have a better sense of smell than has man. This has been partly predicated by the fact that the smelling part of the brain, in some animals, is considerably larger with respect to the whole nervous system, than it is in man. It is highly doubtful that animals have any better smell discrimination than man. It so happens that animals depend for survival more on this kind of discrimination than does man. He has an extraordinary capacity for turning off and on his attention to any particular sensation, and ignoring all others. He has not been dependent upon the sense of smell and his attention is rarely focused on it unless he happens to be a tea taster or a wine taster. Apparently, these unusual abilities for discrimination are quite automatic, in one sense of the word; you either have them or you do not. You either have color discrimnation, musical discrimination, or taste discrimination, depending upon the arrangement of the nerve cells in your cortex. It is equally clear, however, that the basic inherited abilities — to see, to hear, to taste — can be improved manifestly by practice and experience or, if you like, by education. The nerve cell is endowed with certain basic properties and, like muscles, the more those properties are exercised, the more effective becomes the system. The result of all the discriminations and integrations within the cortex, moreover, needs some outward evidence of it through behavior. It is not enough to put information into the nervous system. It has to be coordinated, discriminated, integrated, compared with other bits of information and actually carried through to motor activity. This is why painters paint, musicians play instruments, and why in nearly all the science courses in the country, students go through laboratories. All these methods are examples of the behavior activity expressed in motor patterns which result from the activity of the cortex, and the whole arc must be completed before the nervous system can be able to express effectively what goes on in the cortex. It is quite true that practice makes perfect, that by practice we can develop the expressive sides of the neural activity with much greater effectiveness than the untrained individual. This is so obvious that it hardly needs emphasis but, of course, this is the kind of thing that every child learns as he grows. The only difficulty is that practice, for many people, can be and often is tedious, and most of us tend to quit practice before we acquire any significant efficiency in the motor output.

There is another aspect of the brain of man which is fully as important as the capacity for discrimination, for receiving bits of information, comparing them and bringing about an appropriate response, and that is the strange property of the nervous system which we call memory. We do not know what memory is except by what it does to the behavior of the organism. It seems pretty clear that the bits of information fed into the nervous system by eye and ear, or taste and touch, are stored somewhere in the nervous system in a very interesting fashion. The distinguished neurosurgeon, Wilder Penfield, has been able to show that there are certain parts of the brain in which at least some of the memories of the given individual seem to be stored. Under proper conditions, they can be elicited by external, artificial stimulation. Some have gone so far as to say that no bit of information ever poured into the nervous system is lost; it is all stored in the nervous system. It may be that these stored bits of information are maintained by what is called the reverberating feed-back circuit of the neurones of the cortex. Whatever the basis for memory, the really intriguing aspect of memory is the problem of how the nervous system can unlock, on demand, these sources of information. Human memory, as we all know, is fallible. We often find difficulty in recapturing a bit of information poured into our nervous systems even minutes ago, let alone days, or weeks, or months past. It would be very nice if we could develop a technique by which we could unlock any given memory at any time as desired but, so far as is known, the capacity to do this is still quite definitely limited. Whatever may eventually turn out to be the basis for the capacity of the nervous system to store bits of information in memory banks, as they can be called, it seems reasonably clear that memory has become a part of the integrating, coordinating system of the cortex. Any bit of information coming into man's mind at one instant can always be compared to similar bits of information that have been brought into the nervous system at some previous date. This process, of course, is quite below the level of what is normally called consciousness. Apparently, it goes on in the nervous system automatically, so it is clear that some people have better memories than others. Some have visual memories, remember a written page or even an act of Shakespeare for weeks and months after having read it once; or a musician can play a tune by ear, having heard it at some previous date. In any event, all this information coming into the cortex, built up into discriminations and compared to memories, gives the human nervous system quite extraordinary capacities.

It also has its difficulties, however. We must remember that reflex activity and automatic activity are inherited patterns. We are born with them. Normally, so far as we know, we do not change them to any great extent, but the cortex, the brain of man, the so-called rational part of his being, obviously increases the range of behavior to an enormous extent, and it is not surprising that many of the behavior patterns called forth by the cortex may be different from those that are built into the inherited system. This is a curious aspect of the maturation or the growing up of the nervous system in evolution. All animals have reflexes; all animals have automatic behavior to such an extent that all of us have behavior patterns that are characteristic of the lower animals. We have behavior patterns that are characteristic of fish, of amphibia, of birds, of mammals and of monkeys. These behavior patterns are rigidly determined. They form the basis for virtually all of our motor activity, but it should be quite clear that the behavior of a fish does not help the behavior of a bird very much, nor does a bird's behavior help the mammal's behavior. All through the nervous system, therefore, there are groups of neurones whose job it is to submerge some of these older behavior patterns or perhaps, better yet, to make use of them in the much more complex behavior patterns of the human. As children grow up, they exhibit many motor patterns which are characteristic of lower vertebrates. These disappear as he is growing. His nervous system regulates the appearance of these old patterns, makes use of them where they contribute to the wholeness of the behavior of the organism or submerges them if they come into conflict with these higher patterns. As a result of this, the development of the ten billion cells of the cortex has introduced a confusing factor into behavior. Because of the enormous competence of this cortex, and because of the great variety of behavior patterns which it can invoke, often it may result in conflict in the expressive behavior of the organism.

It will be worthwhile here to turn our attention to some of these conflicting elements in expressive behavior which have resulted from the development of this cortical addition to the basic properties of the elementary nervous system. Every living system demands chemical substances for its continued existence. These are vital. Just as you cannot run an automobile without gasoline, so biological systems cannot exist without food. All the food in the world, however, no matter how carefully selected, cannot change in any significant fashion the structure of the human nervous system. It can enable the neural mechanisms to live; it can provide the structure with the necessary energy for its operation, but never can it put anything into the system which was not there originally. The only thing the chemical environment can do, so far as anybody knows, is either to help the living system to achieve maximum control over its functional activity, or to damage some part of its responding system. Chemistry creates nothing new in the living system.

In many ways, then, the nervous system is like an enormous computer. The cortex receives information from the outside as well as the inside environment. It there discriminates, coordinates, compares with the past experience of all sort of valuable and exceedingly varied data. In other words, he thinks. In common terms, he has a mind. Unfortunately he, in his vanity, is sure he creates his mind. He does not. To be sure, by practice, the reactions within the cortex become more efficient. In some mysterious way, moreover, new paths of nerve impulses may connect one group of nerve cells with another group hitherto not involved in cortical activity. Thus man invents, imagines, sees visions and, perhaps most important of all, sets up through these new functional pathways symbols, a sort of shorthand which stands for galaxies of events in the world outside himself. Thus he may perceive new relationships between things seen or heard. He can be said to create something new, but only in the sense that because of the myriads of cells in the cortex, previously unoccupied neural channels become functional. But man does not have unlimited capacities. Because of the very great numbers of possible connections, it would seem as though he could accomplish anything he desired, as though he had complete freedom of choice. This is not so. The only freedom he has is to choose between a number of possibles. Such possibles are definitely limited by the arrangement of the nerve cells he inherits. We cannot all be great painters, musicians or writers. Only those with particular nerve patterns can become truly great in certain areas of activity, and these are determined. They are not a matter of choice. Man, if he is lucky, may discover some ability in himself. He then has the choice of exploiting, practicing that capacity until it reaches its maximum competence. Thus mathematicians, dancers, acrobats practice their abilities until they often become well-nigh perfect. Here, again, the perfection achieved is not just a matter of desire, but rather of the effectiveness of the nerve arrangements.

Your behavior and mine, then, springs from the nerve patterns of our cortical gray matter working through the quite rigid non-modifiable and automatic neural mechanisms of the spinal cord, the cerebellum and the basal ganglia. These congeries of nerves determine behavior. They make us what we are. Through their control of the activity of expressive behavior, they make it possible to recognize a certain individual as a unique personality.

Chapter VI

THE SENSE OF WELL-BEING

THE EVIDENCE makes it abundantly clear that your behavior
and mine is a consequence of a particular pattern of organization
of your nervous system and of mine. Myriads of cells which
make up those nervous systems endow it with properties which
are not inherent in any of its component parts which arise from
the combinations, the relationships of these component parts.
The sets of forces which impose the necessary relationships between the component parts of the nervous system must be of
great power and must provide the very important directional
properties of the activities of living systems. These patterns
of organization, in other words, are not the result of accident,
but are the result of the operation of a rigidly determined force-
ful control over the movement of all charged particles within the whole living system and of the direction in which energy will flow within the system. The nervous system, then,
provides the living system with the one thing which has not
been recognized widely in biology — a set of vector forces.
These are forces which give direction to the whole problem
of organization of protoplasm and its functional activity. You
and I, like all other living systems, are electrical fields. These
fields are primary. They determine the arrangements of the
parts of the living system and control, to a very considerable degree, most of its activities. The most perfect example of this
kind of control is found in the design and the functional activity
of the human nervous system.

We have seen that there are at least four kinds of controls
over the activity of our bodies, over the thing we call human
behavior. The most complex of these controls is that which
emanates from the neurones of the cerebral cortex, the gray
matter of the brain, but includes also the inherited, automatic,

associated patterns mediated by the nuclear masses at the base of the brain, the basal ganglia, the automatic balancing mechanisms supplied by the brain stem and cerebellum, and finally the reflex activities of the spinal cord and its peripheral nerves. Four kinds of control of behavior, therefore, can be recognized, but perhaps the most astonishing thing of the whole nervous system is the fact that these controls all find expression through the activity of motor cells lodged in the ventral lateral regions of the spinal cord. These have been called anterior motor horn cells, or the final common pathway. They are rather large neurones whose axis cylinders run out to muscle, over which neural messages may be sent for appropriate control. It would take too long to enumerate all the pathways from higher centers in the nervous system which finally impinge on these anterior motor horn cells, but there are very many of them; so many, in fact, that it is astonishing that a single anterior motor horn cell can take all this information sent down to it from areas higher up in the brain and make sense out of them.

In many ways, these anterior motor horn cells are a sort of information center collecting bits of information from all over the nervous system, pouring them into this one neural mechanism and there, in some mysterious fashion, they are analyzed, put together, coordinated, integrated and eventually result in the formation of neural impulses which constitute an appropriate response to all the information delivered to that particular center. The success of the integrations within this motor neurone is extraordinary. To be sure, it has been conditioned by eons of time in the evolution of living organisms, has probably increased its effectiveness as a result of daily experience, but still the job it does is almost beyond human comprehension. It must be clear that to operate effectively, most of the information sent to it from higher areas in the central nervous system must have already undergone a number of combinations and coordinations in the higher centers. The most complicated of all these controls, of course, is the cerebral cortex. With its infinitude of neurones, the possibilities of all the permutations and combinations of their interactions are astronomical. The great variety of such possible connections makes it appear as though the cortex were an area where anything may happen. To a limited extent, this is true, but it must not be forgotten that the nerve fibers which connect neurones in one part of the gray matter to another are included in the original pattern of organization of the nervous system. Some people like to think that the pathway which these neurones take through the neural cortex can be changed by practice and experience, or by education. There is not a trace of evidence to indicate that that is true. We are born with these connections. There seems to be little doubt about that, and because we are born with these connections, there are certain things that we, as human beings, can do and there are certain things we very obviously cannot do. This is not a matter of practice nor of education. This is a matter of particular machinery which constitutes you and me. While it is clear that these structural connections, between parts of the cortex, are inherited, determined by the pattern of organization of the nervous system, it is equally clear that the functional efficiency of certain connections may be greater than others. In other words, the connections of nerve cells within the cortex endow it, functionally, with certain predilections. As a result, there are certain kinds of behavior which dominate the whole pattern of activity of any one human. It is quite probable that these dominant pathways, both structurally and functionally, are the things which endow each of us with that strange thing which we know as personality. We know personality only through the behavior of the people with whom we come in contact. This behavior, as we have seen, is a function of the connections of the nervous system.

It is equally clear, however, that the structure does not tell the whole story. One of the very interesting things about the evolution of living things is the fact that structure appears before function — long before function — that it takes time, probably long stretches of time before a structurally organized protoplasmic system acquires functional maturity. This is simply another way of saying that in the evolution of living organisms in general, and in man in particular, the same kind of maturation process has gone on that can be recognized in a growing child.

It is well-known that the neurones of the whole nervous system and of the cortex are present, and active to a limited extent, at birth. From then on, the process of the acquisition of functional maturity is a process in which experience and education activate previously determined structural pathways. Repeated neural impulses over these pathways increase, unquestionably, the efficiency with which those pathways work. This is the hope of education. But there is one serious difficulty in this whole business. In many ways gray matter of the cortex, as has been suggested, operates like our modern electronic computers. It does it, of course, with an infinitely small fraction of the power required to operate a modern electronic computer. It does it, on the whole, with much greater efficiency, but the nervous system, unlike the computer, makes some kind of sense out of every bit of information that comes in. This is something which no man-made computer can do, for it has to have the right kind of information poured into it in the correct sets of formulae, or programs, as they are called. So far as anyone knows, mankind has no particular programming mechanism. Rather the programming seems to be a built-in function of the interconnections between the neurones. The computer has to have the right kind of information poured into it in the right ways, but the human nervous system can take all kinds of information — good, bad and indifferent — and coordinate and discriminate so that, as a result, there comes out some kind of reasonably coordinated behavior. Now in spite of the fact that the behavior of many of us can be called at least bizarre, it is, nevertheless, a highly coordinated, integrated business. On the other hand, random bits of information poured into the electronic computers do not come out with an organized answer. It would be very nice if we could be sure that only the right kinds of information were poured in through eye and ear, and so on, so that the results of the integration would always be ideal. Unfortunately, this is not true. We do not know enough about human beings and their behavior to be able to say, without argument, that this is the right bit of information for that particular kind of neural mechanism. As a matter of fact, through our educational procedures and our experience, the nervous system is bombarded by an infinitude of bits of information which, somehow or other, can be built into an appropriate response. This response is a very important thing. What constitutes an adequate response for you is not necessarily the right behavior for me. As we have seen, the human being is a unique individual like nothing else in the Universe — more complicated than anything else in the Universe except the Universe itself. The capacity of the brain of man to initiate appropriate responses to this enormous source of information is one of the great mysteries of living organisms. We do not know how it is accomplished. We have no clue to the mechanism that is involved in the brain's automatic programming of all the bits of information that come into it. There is no doubt, however, that such programming exists.

One very interesting consequence of the multitudinous components of the cortex and their astronomical interconnections is the fact that incoming bits of information may travel over pathways hitherto unused. As a result, the mind of man sees new and unsuspected relationships between the bits of information which he receives. These new relationships and new discriminations, these new comparisons are the basic material out of which is built the enormously valuable aspect of the mind of man, the imagination. It has been said by very distinguished scientists that the activity which we know as imaginative cannot be demanded by the individual. There are no rules nor regulations by which we can order the neurones to acquire new functional activities. As a matter of fact, they never create new connections because those are predetermined, but they do emphasize certain pathways over others, and this brings about a different kind of appropriate response. This capacity of the mind of man to imagine, to create symbols, to see new ways of solving the bits of information that are poured into the nervous system is one of the most valuable aspects of the functional activity of the human brain. It is no wonder that mankind has invented the soul, or a mind to explain this apparently mysterious self-programming of the neurones of the cortex. That it exists, there can be no question, but our uderstanding is much too limited for us to provide an adequate explanation of how it works. Because the structural interconnections of the gray matter of the cortex is a predetermined thing, it is not surprising that man has tried to endow himself with a control of behavior which is rational, so far as he can tell. He thinks, in other words, that somehow or other he can program the bits of information in certain characteristic ways so that it will produce a kind of behavior which seems to be divorced from haphazard or accidental activity. So man seems to have endowed himself with the kind of activity which can be called logical, that there are some necessary relationships between what has happened and what will happen, some kind of orderly regulation of the responses to the outside stimuli. It has also been said by distinguished scientists that logic, in the last analysis, is the way the mind of man works. Perhaps this is why so many computers are built around systems of logic. The function of the cortex, the thing we call the mind of man, does seem to exhibit certain properties which suggest that it operates according to the laws of logic. We have seen also that it has the extraordinary ability to see new and unexpected relationships, in other words, to have the capacity for imagination.

But there is a third attribute of the cortex. It is the strange thing we call intuition. This is a curious, automatic synthesis of widely divergent kinds of information. These scattered bits, most of which are rarely in the area of what we know as consciousness, nevertheless, can be combined and re-combined in new ways or, if you like, synthesized, to produce a new kind of an appropriate response. This leads to what are often believed to be quite miraculous guesses which the mind of man makes about the meaning and importance of things outside of himself. He is said to intuit the significance and meaning and importance of this set of outside events. It must be kept constantly in mind that the gray matter of the cortex receives enormous numbers of bits of information from a wide variety of sources and in some apparently mysterious way is able to elaborate the rational, the imaginative, and the intuitive behavior patterns of the organism. These are really the important functional activities of the gray matter. So far as is known, none of the man-made computers can compare with the human nervous system in reaching these heights of control. To be sure, the computers learn by experience, but so does protoplasm. To be sure, the right kind of information, sent in to the right kind of program, can produce the right kind of an answer with a greater efficiency, with greater speed than do the neurones of the cortex, but the neurones of the cortex require only a microscopic fraction of the energy required by the computers. The fear has sometimes been expressed that in due time the machines that man creates will take over the business of running the Universe and relegate man, therefore, to a very minor and unimportant aspect. This fear of machine dominance of civilization is most certainly sheer and unadulterated nonsense. We have been bemused by the apparent efficiency of man-made machines. They are incredibly efficient. There is no argument about that; but man can do far more than any machine because he creates the machine. Through his rational, imaginative and intuitive powers he can design, devise and build these automatic gadgets. Man, however, has his own built-in programming device; the computers have no such thing. Some external agent — mankind — has to do this for the machine. This will always be true. The machines can do extraordinary things, but they cannot do them without the interference of the human nervous system.

It must not be forgotten, of course, that this cortical control of behavior is only one of the various regulations which the nervous system exerts over the muscles of movement. It has to work through automatic, associated controls of the basal ganglia, the automatic balancing of the brain stem and cerebellum, and the reflex controls of the spinal cord. Interestingly enough, as we have seen in the long history of evolution, Nature has never, or almost never, discarded any part of the neural mechanism; she has simply added new ones to it. These new mechanisms exert some kind of regulation over the inherited neural patterns. All of these added arrangements are aimed at making it possible for the living organism, including you and me, to adjust more adequately to its environment. The older controls, emanating from nuclear masses that lie beneath the cortex, and hence sometimes called sub-cortical controls, are strictly inherited patterns and are quite clearly non-modifiable. They can be regulated so that parts of them can be prevented from obstructing behavior pattern. Others can be accentuated to increase the effectiveness of these responses. The standard term used for these kinds of controls is *inhibition,* which is a curious word that means to stop activities of certain kinds.

Since the cortex, with its extraordinary capacity of discrimination and integration, is able not only to bring about some kind of appropriate motor response but is able to synthesize or create symbols for certain kinds of combinations of things outside themselves, we have called these symbolizations of outside information, ideas. The really extraordinary thing about this whole business is the fact that an idea is just as much of a stimulus to the human nervous system as is a poke in the eye. They are very real, so far as the nervous system is concerned. It is very clear from the history of mankind that an idea can be far more important than any other single set of stimuli which the human nervous system receives. Virtually everything that we do stems sooner or later from the ideas which have originated in the complexity of combinations within the neurones of the human brain. So far as man is concerned, ideas are explosive. They provide him with all of his capacities to dominate his physical and chemical environment. Man could have survived for only a very short time if he had not been able to create ideas out of incoming bits of information and, through intuition and imagination and logic, convert them into obvious, describable gadgets, gadgets which protect us from the inimical factors in our physical and chemical environment — see further, hear further, move faster — than any other living system. Ideas, then, seem to be the crowning capacity of the human cortex. They come out of an automatic synthesis of bits of information through intuition and imagination and logic into that kind of automatic adjustment to the physical and chemical and idealogical environment that makes it possible for man to dominate any environment in which he finds himself. But ideas, like all the other functions of the cortex, must operate through the lower-lying centers in the nervous system. Here, of course, is one of the still unsolved problems of human behavior. Most of us, in our ordinary activity, presumably use our cortex for an astonishingly small part of the time. Virtually all the activities in which we are engaged, are automatic. We are born with them. We do not have to send particular messages to the muscles of the leg and of the thigh and of the trunk, which result in ordinary movements for walking. These are managed by the automatic centers in the basal ganglia, in the cerebellum, and in the spinal cord. It must be remembered that these are highly efficient mechanisms. They have been conditioned by eons of time in the evolution of the nervous system. They have proved themselves successful, because living systems have survived over the long ages of evolution. One of the consequences of these automatic, inherited controls of behavior are those strange things which we call emotions. To many people, these are the most important things in life. They give color to the living organsm, activate his whole system with somewhat greater force than do perhaps the activities of the cortex; they are characteristic of the individual; they are, in many senses of the word, the stuff of life. To many, it is only through the emotions that we can really express adequately what we euphemistically call ourselves.

But it must not be forgotten that these emotions are not the consequence of the functioning of the cerebral cortex. Emotions are the product of inherited patterns, so that many aspects of our behavior are quite automatic and recognizable as being common properties of all human beings. Most of us do the same things when we are angry, when we hate, when we love, when we are hungry. These age-old patterns of the control of behavior, which exert rather astonishing control over automatic balance and reflexes, also send a great deal of information into the cortex. This means, of course, that the cortex receives not only a lot of information from outside the organism, but a lot of information from inside the organism. As a result, most of the activities of the cortex are not isolated phenomena, but are bound up, interrelated, and closely tied to the emotional output of basal ganglia mechanisms. Man likes to think of himself as a rational animal, that in his highest forms of activity he rises above these inherited patterns, patterns which the religionists have often called "the beast in us." As a matter of fact, the rational activity of the cortex can never be separated from the emotional components of the basal ganglia. Furthermore, not only are these emotional dabs of information sent to the cortex but also the cortex, after receiving all this information, and perhaps storing some of it in memory, sends it back down to the basal ganglia nuclei. When these new integrations within the cortex, colored by emotional content, are sent back to the basal ganglia to regulate their activity so that there is a proper balance between the emotional and the rational, the individual then reaches a state which is sometimes known as a sense of well-being. This is a kind of internal harmony, an internal balance between cortical and basal ganglia mechanisms. Ideally, this is the ultimate goal of the nervous system, to provide the organism with an adequate sense of well-being. When these interconnections between basal ganglia and cortex result in functional activity which is in harmony — an internal harmony — then the sense of well-being can be said to exist. All of the idealogical activities of the human cortex must be charged by the emotional content derived from the functions of the basal ganglia. It is unfortunate, however, that some of the automatic, associated movements, mediated through the basil ganglia, some of our automatic emotions, are not really conducive to well-being in the idealogical world of the cortex, but it is part of the components of the nervous system that these two kinds of control be harmonized in some effective way. As we shall see later, in the absence of this internal harmony, the behavior of man becomes difficult to understand and, therefore, difficult to adjust to.

The nervous system, of course, requires energy for its operation and the sources of energy, as we have seen, are the chemical factories of the body. The nuclei at the base of the brain, the basal ganglia, in addition to being the seat of the patterns which result in what we call our emotions, control the chemical factories of the body. For that reason they are a vital, important and, in many instances, a dominating factor in the kind of behavior which you and I exhibit. All nerve cells require energy, but not all nerve cells demand the same kind. There is a very real probability that each kind of neurone, grouped in functionally comparable mechanisms, demands and gets different kinds of chemical energy. When this energy is available, these systems operate effectively; when it is not, the reverse may be true and behavior may be stultified by its absence. This also, is true, that to many, this means that the answers to all the problems that man is heir to are to be found in chemistry, that by feeding certain kinds of chemical agents, certain factors in the nervous system can be made to dominate the control of human behavior and, as a result, someday we should be able to rectify any kind of misbehavior by giving the individual certain kinds of chemical substances. Now for the basal ganglia to activate the chemical factories of the body to provide the right kind of energy means that they must be working at top efficiency all of the time. The pouring of chemicals into the blood stream, required by the nerves of the brain, is a highly complex and quite automatic business. The raw material of ingested food must be processed through the digestive system, circulated through the blood vessels by means of the heart, reinforced by chemials elaborated in special organs for the purpose, such as the liver and the adrenals, and so on. The chemical factories of the body are so complex, so incredibly efficient, that man-kind in spite of all of his creative ability is just beginning to duplicate the simplest forms of the chemical substances made by living stuff. The infinitely precise controls required, obviously cannot work in the face of constant interference from the cortex. It takes very little to upset these precise mechanisms. It is not surprising, therefore, that there has developed a whole new branch of medicine — phychosomatic medicine — which concerns itself, primarily, with the physiological consequences of ideas impinging on basal ganglia mechanisms and, therefore, on the emotions, and producing such confusion that much of the activity of automatic mechanisms within the living organism are thrown out of kilter. It is well-known, of course, that if certain areas in the base of the brain are damaged by disease, or by interference from the cortex, erosion in the wall of the stomach which we know as ulcers, follows. This is simply evidence of the fact that the cortex and the basal ganglia mechanisms must act harmoniously unless there are to be dire consequences so far as the organism itself is concerned. The really astonishing thing about this whole business is how effectively the emotional and basal ganglia controls of automatic activity are exerted. Most of us get along, much of the time, with relatively little difficulty in these matters; in fact, many of the difficulties that arise come from the fact that the rational mind of man tries to improve upon these age-old and well-conditioned basal ganglia controls. The cortex, you will remember, is a relatively recent addition to the nervous system; but the basal ganglia, brain stem and cerebellum and spinal cord are old — as old as backbone animals. All these mechanisms have been conditioned by experience to become highly effective controlling mechanisms. They have matured; their patterns of organization have been practiced until they are perfect. The cortex, a relatively new addition to the family of controls, has not had such conditioning by time, has not matured in the same sense as the rest of the nervous system, and it is not surprising, therefore, that many of the activities of the cortex tend to interfere with these mature, age-old, genetically determined and non-modifiable behavior patterns of basal ganglia.

Over the centuries, many men have dreamed of being completely rational, able to behave in a completely logical manner and they tend to pride themselves on the fact that they are able to divorce themselves from the primitive and uncontrolled emotional content of all of our activities. This, of course, is sheer, unadulterated nonsense. No man can ever be completely rational and, because man has a cortex, he can never be completely emotional. If he is completely emotional, in a very real sense of the word, he is an undeveloped individual. The fact that emotions provide color and some of the excitement of life leads many people to think that this is the highest level of human activity. These are the people who maintain that the primitive in all the things that man has done over the years is really, basically, the central characteristic of human behavior. This, of course, is nonsense; it is not so; the primitive is interesting historically, perhaps, but it is completely devoid of any of the content provided by the logical, imaginative, intuitive, and discriminative functions of the cortex. Emotional life is devoid of ideas, devoid of the highest functional components of the human nervous system. Moreover, it is the kind of behavior that is quite uncharacteristic of man. Remember, that man is uniquely individual. There are no two of us alike. This unique individuality is the consequence of the presence of the gray matter of the cortex. If mankind operated entirely on a sub-cortical level, on the basal ganglia or emotional level, he would no longer be unique; he would be simply one of the herd. Many properties of each of us would be common to all of us and man would lose the one preeminent characteristic which gives him his essential dignity and that is, his capacity to be different, to integrate out of raw material new and interesting, significant, and valuable ways of controlling his own behavior as a means of attaining the goals which follow from the functions of cortical mechanisms. The emotional mechanisms may provide the drive in the sense that gasoline provides the energy which makes an automobile go, but it is the idealogical function of the cortex to provide the goals for which man strives. It is this striving for new goals which is uniquely characteristic of man. Even this unique striving for goals cannot operate without the emotional content of the driving force of the consequences of the chemical factors in the living organism.

If only we knew enough, we ought to be able to pour into the cortex the kind of information which would end in harmonious relationships with the basal ganglia mechanisms. If we could filter out of the information coming into the cortex those bits of information which, integrated and coordinated, would turn out to be not in conflict with basal ganglia control, we would achieve internal harmony. This is the age-old problem of mankind. Human behavior is as varied as the stars, and unfortunately, man, somewhere along the line, probably because of his inability to select the right kind of information, has convinced himself that he knows what is right; that he can, therefore, legislate how the other fellow must behave. Now this legislation of behavior for other people, such as is created by the legalists and by the religionists, is guilty of pouring into the cortex bits of information which, when integrated, discriminated and rationalized are in conflict with the age-old controls of the basal ganglia. In a very real sense of the word, man-made laws are in conflict with the laws of nature. This, obviously, is absurd. If man is going to make rules and regulations to control the behavior of other people he should, of course, start first of all with himself and then, if applied to other people, must be in harmonious relationship to natural law, not in conflict with it. It would follow from all this, therefore, that many of our difficulties in modern living are made by the disregard of human beings for the uniquely individual capacities of each of us. What law-makers say, when it is unrelated to basal ganglia activities, is to produce confusion. When the moralists say this is right and that is bad, they are obviously disregarding the fact that they do not know what is right or what is bad, for what is right for me is, by no manner of means, necessarily right for you, except purely on a basal ganglia level, and we are not basal ganglia animals. We are cortical animals and as such it behooves us to do our level best to relate the kinds of information that are poured into the human cortex to the basic biological laws which have determined the creation and functional activity of the whole nervous system, instead of arbitrarily deciding what is right for the other fellow. In the last analysis, there is only one answer to the question to what is right or what is wrong. What is true is right; what is false is wrong. This, of course, is an arbitrary statement and many people will resent it, because they have firmly planted in their cortices the belief that truth is an eternal factor, not subject to change or modification and, therefore, what is right or what is wrong has exacting standards. In the ideal sense, this is probably correct, but in actual practice mankind does not know all there is to know about everything; he does not know the truth. Our understanding of the nature of the Universe is a constantly changing thing. This is obvious as we survey the history of science. Truth changes its garments from age to age, and what was right when one kind of understanding was true, will not necessarily fit with our present understanding of what is true. What we believe to be true now, moreover, is not by any manner of means the final answer. Each age contributes new understanding of the nature of truth and, as such, our convictions as to the nature of right and wrong are bound to change. That ultimately there is some kind of truth in the Universe, cannot be denied. The Universe is a place of law and order which the mind of man can comprehend, but it is going to take time and our advance toward this ultimate goal is a slow and, to many people, an apparently wasteful process and, as such, is often discouraging. To the contrary, it is exciting, because it gives all of us an opportunity to strive toward a better understanding of what is true and, therefore, a clearer picture of what is right and what is wrong.

From all this argument, it should be apparent that the functioning of the nervous system, as a whole, in order to maintain this sense of well-being, is an extremely, finely adjusted mechanism such that each component part contributes productively to the activities of the whole. Only when this happens can it be said that man is well-adjusted. Only then can it be said that man is paradic, that is to say, that he functions in accordance with his design.

Chapter *VII*

THE ANATOMY OF ANXIETY

To EVERY generation comes the conviction that its problems
are greater than those ever encountered by mankind. From the
beginning, man has been troubled and he is rather inclined to
think that his troubles are unique, never have been met before,
presenting problems which are difficult, if not impossible of
solution. This worries many people, but it should not. Man is
a living system and, like every living system, he is constantly
trying to reach some kind of satisfactory adjustment to all the
impulses that fall upon him during his lifetime. In one sense
of the word, just the business of living is a struggle to maintain
adequate and satifactory relationships with his environment.
As we have seen, throughout his life his nervous system receives
multitudinous stimuli of all kinds — eye and ear, and other
sensory mechanisms. In spite of certain relatively rigid and
predetermined computer-like properties, the nervous system ab-
sorbs all these stimuli and programs them in such a fashion
that they provide the individual with an adjustment to his
environment which, for most of us, most of the time, is reasonably satisfactory.

It will be remembered further that one of the great attributes
of the human nervous system is its ability to create out of all
this special sense information symbols or, perhaps even better,
ideas. It is equally clear also that these ideas are just as valid,
so far as the operation of the nervous system is concerned, as
any other kind of stimulus reaching it. Ideas are supremely
important. They make it possible for a man to create new and
wonderful things. Most of the boasted advances in civilization
have come from ideas. On the other hand, an idea can be just
as destructive as an atomic bomb, or a hurricane, or a tornado.
It is well-known, of course, that many of the great changes which

have occurred in the history of civilization have come out of the ideas of individual men. Such ideas have changed the face of the world.

Thus there are two kinds of stimuli adequate for the activation of the nervous system. One set of such stimuli are those, of course, of a physical nature — sight and sound — but the other is just as important an activity — the creation within the nervous system of ideas. The entrance of these different kinds of stimuli — what may be called the physical stimuli on the one hand, and the idealogical stimuli on the other — must be harmonized if we are to achieve any sense of well-being. In addition to these external stimuli there are, of course, the innumerable bits of information derived from all the parts of the body. From these sources the nervous system tries to maintain the internal environment of the human body at a reasonably adequate level, thus creating in the individual the sense of well-being. This occurs only when the chemistry of the body is under adequate coordination, for every minutest corner of the body is constantly sending stimuli through nerves into the central nervous system. When these are put together in an adequate fashion, there is developed an internal harmony, the kind of thing a great physiologist called *homeostasis,* a reasonable constancy of the internal chemistry. These two sets of stimuli — first, those that come in from outside of the body, through the special senses, and the second, the stimuli that arise within the organism itself — reach quite different areas in the nervous system.

So far as we know, the capacity to create ideas is almost entirely a function of the cortex. As we have seen, however, the cortex never acts entirely independently of the rest of the nervous system but is always in close contact with all the activities of the rest of the nervous system. On the other hand, the sense of well-being is derived almost entirely from internal stimuli, stimuli derived from organ systems of the body. It will be remembered that these two components of the nervous system have quite different evolutionary histories. The cortex, where ideas are generated, is a relatively new addition to the nervous system of the higher animals and man. The areas of the nervous system which are bound up in the maintenance of the internal harmony of the body, on the other hand, are age-old; they go back to the very beginning of the organization of a specialized neural mechanism. The neurones which are involved in this internal harmony are grouped together as the basal ganglia. They are concerned, primarily, with automatic adjustment of the living system to its physical environment. These automatic patterns are characteristic of the species to which the animal belongs. They provide the motor activity by which we recognize the living system as a man or as an animal. These patterns are inherited patterns that have been conditioned by the eons of time involved in the evolution of the nervous system. So far as we know, the automatic mechanisms of the basal ganglia, inherited as they are, are subject to very little, if any, modification. To be sure, practice and experience may increase the efficiency of the patterns, but it does not introduce into the nervous system any new patterns. For this reason, for many people, these represent the automatic, instinctive adjustment which the animal or man makes to his environment. They are the automatic activities which are involved in courtship, in mating, in fighting, in feeding — all the manifold mechanisms by which the living system is enabled to maintain its bodily form in the face of a constant, chemical flux and by means of which it avoids inimical factors in the environment, even combating these factors in rage and anxiety.

Unlike the basal ganglia, the cortex of man, apparently, can be educated, but this does not mean, as we have seen, that education creates new structural connections within the brain, but rather that in the process of education pre-formed pathways become functionally dominant and, therefore, exert an increasingly important control over motor activities.

Within the basal ganglia there are two sets of neurones, one of which is an arrival platform for all forms of bodily sensation. The thalamus, to which these sensations come, provides coordination and integration, the result of which is a crude awareness of the state of the body, of its position in space and of its movement. This awareness is of a very crude sort. Normally, we are not conscious of it. It has little or no discrimination. We know roughly where our arms and hands and feet are; we can tell whether or not we have on gloves or shoes. General patterns of information from various parts of the body lack critical discrimination so that we cannot be certain just exactly what part of the upper or lower extremity is being stimulated, nor how great the difference is in the kinds of touch which are applied to the skin, the kind of pain which may result in injury to the skin, nor does it make possible the identification of the exact place where a pin pricks the skin. The integrations within this sensory nucleus, the thalamus, provide man with the information that is necessary for him to adjust adequately to his physical environment, both external and internal. It makes it possible for him to make all kinds of — complicated to be sure, but nevertheless, automatic — adjustments to this physical environment. The thalamus, then, the sensory part of the basal ganglia, is the arrival platform of stimuli from all over the body and provides the individual with a curious kind of integration which has many names, but which most of us understand best by the term, *the emotional set,* or attitude. This emotional set has many valuable attributes. In the first place, they are characterized by quite typical ways of self-expression. Thus we can recognize the emotions of other people, which give color and excitement to virtually all of our activities. The reason for this is not hard to see, because it must be remembered that within this basal ganglia complex lie the neural mechanisms which are concerned, primarily, with the regulation of the chemical factories of the body. These provide the energy by which the nervous system operates and, so far as anyone knows, the kind of energy that is a necessary requirement for our emotions. They are as necessary as fuel is to any engine whose efficiency is, in part, a function of the availability of those chemicals which can be readily converted into its energy requirements. Again, the neuronal patterns involved in the integrations within the thalamus are non-modifiable ways of doing things. They have persisted through eons of time and have been highly successful.

But the basal ganglia consists of something more than just

the arrival platform for the physical environment of a living organism. It has built into it, neurones which are primarily concerned with the necessary motor activity, the end result of which is the adequate adjustment by movement of the body to the crude awareness and emotional controls of the sensory component of the basal ganglia. These motor acts, again, are inherited patterns. They are determined and to a very considerable extent, are non-modifiable or, in other words, they cannot, on the whole, be taught very much. One cannot see any evidence, in other words, that new patterns of these automatic adjustments occur during the life of a human being. It is clear enough that these motor acts we recognize as love, hate, rage, result from the integrations within the thalamus and involve relatively simple kinds of activity — the rhythmic movements of the fins, the alternate contractions and relaxations of muscles along the back, all the kinds of movements which are characteristic of a particular animal. During the long process of evolution these have become increasingly complex until in man, these automatic associated movements, as they are called, are really quite complex. They are so complete, in fact, for nearly all animals, that they are quite adequate for continued survival. In all probability, virtually all animals below man, certainly below mammals, react through the neural patterns of the motor mechanisms of the basal ganglia. These motor paths have been proven successful throughout the process of evolution. They have selected and practiced to the point where they provide the organism with very adequate survival capacity in meeting the problems of the physical environment. All these patterns, moreover, no matter how complex they are, become one of the identifying characteristics of particular kinds of animals. The difference between the gait of a horse and of man, a cat, or a mouse are examples of this kind of automatic behavior. It is this series of neurones in the basal ganglia which are primarily concerned with the automatic and adequate adjustment of the organism to its physical environment. So far as anyone knows, there is no evidence whatever that the distance receptors — vision and hearing and smell — are involved to any great extent in these patterns. As we shall see eventually, there is some relationship between them, but it is not a primary one, because this region of the nervous system has no direct connections with either eye or ear. Now one of the very interesting things about this group of neurones at the base of the brain, is that in the development of the brain they give rise to large numbers of wandering neurones, nerve cells, that leave these basal ganglia regions and migrate to the surface of the brain where they lay down the cortex. In the process of wandering from central gray to the surface of the brain, functional relationships are established connecting the basal ganglia to the cortex. Thus the cortex is, in part, an enormous expansion of basal ganglia activities. It has been shown that many lower animals can get along very well without a cortex, so long as their basal ganglia are still intact. But more important than any of these aspects of the problem is the fact that the fiber tract connections between basal ganglia and cortex carry emotional color and excitement into the complex neural mechanism of the cortex. To the cortex, the distance receptors — vision and hearing — bring all kinds of information from the outside world where they meet the upsurging emotional content of the basal ganglia. All the creative imaginings and discriminations of the cortex are colored and vivified by the emotional overflow from the primitive brain. Every idea, then, is deeply colored by emotion. This is of major importance because it makes it abundantly clear that the cortex can never operate independently of the basal ganglia. As we have seen, man likes to think of himself as a rational animal, something over and above and better than the so-called beast in us. This is nonsense, because the cortex is tied so tightly to the functions of the basal ganglia that it never can operate independently of it. The cortex, moreover, has its fiber connections by which sight and sound, and the emotions can be converted into expressive behavior, that is to say, into voluntary actions. One stretches out one's hand to pick up a glass of water. This is voluntary. It is easy to think that that is all there is to that kind of movement — just the volition to do it — but it is far more complex than that, because the neurones which initiate this movement do not act only by themselves; they act through the motor mechanisms of the basal ganglia, the cerebellum and the spinal cord. They do this because not only is there a rich connection between the basal ganglia and cortex, but an equally rich connection from cortex back to basal ganglia so that volition can mobilize the automatic mechanisms of lower centers to control smoothly and adequately the motor pattern which arises in the neural mechanism of the cortex.

These connections from cortex to basal ganglia, however, have another function. Many of the older automatic patterns must be regulated if they are going to take an active part in the smooth control of the voluntary movement, and so the cortex, through its fiber connections to basal ganglia and cerebellum and spinal cord, can control the automatic patterns so that they contribute to smooth movement. It is customary to talk about this regulatory function as an inhibition, a kind of blockage (of lower motor mechanism. The great probability is that this is not strictly a blockage, but is a kind of selective elicitation from the lower centers of automatic controls which conduce to the smooth activity of the so-called volitional motor patterns of the cortex. The very rich connections between basal ganglia and cortex, and cortex and basal ganglia, tie the two mechanisms for the control of behavior into a very tightly organized and coordinated unit. Since all animals without a cortex are entirely automatic in their actions, so man with a cortex can never be entirely an emotional nor automatic animal.

While it is true that the basal ganglia controls have been conditioned by eons of evolutionary time, and have been highly successful in making survival possible, yet the evolution of man has resulted in the appearance of the cortex and, therefore, of new and relatively untried controls of our activities. By virtue of the cortex, the varieties of human experience and behavior have increased enormously. We like to think that this is an improvement, that man is better than the animals, but it must be remembered that the cortex and, therefore, a part at least of human behavior, is quite new. It has not had anything like the trial by fire of the primitive brain. Hence, when it comes to

the problem of adjustment to our physical — not our ideational
— environment the primitive brain can be trusted to do the job
successfully. To be sure, the functions of the cortex constitute
what has been called, for lack of a better term, the mind of
man. It coordinates, integrates, and discriminates to an astonishing degree, by virtue of the enormous increase in the
number of nerve cells involved. The mind of man, nevertheless, never can be completely separated from the mechanisms
of the basal ganglia. In some senses of the word, it can be argued
that the cortex is nothing more nor less than the expansion of
basal ganglia function. It certainly is that, but on top of that
it has functions which the basal ganglia do not possess. The
cortex can discriminate and can coordinate and integrate on a
very much more complicated level than can the basal ganglia.
Because of its manifestly richer sets of attributes, many people
like to think that man is the only really rational animal; that he
can, in a very real sense, react to his environment at a purely
rational or reasonable level, divorced from the beast in him.
This, you will recognize, is the point of view of many people
who think that man, the consequence of long eons of evolution,
has risen above the animal in him. Of course, he has; but he is
an animal and his animal-like activity, his primitive or emotional
behavior, is a very important component of all he does. In
addition to that kind of animal-like behavior, however, he has
the enormous functional efficiency of the cortex endowing him
with the manifold attributes which make him a unique individual. As a consequence, no two of us are alike. To be sure,
we have two hands, two feet, two eyes, and so on, like other
human beings, but when one moves beyond the physical attributes, it is clear that each human being differs from all others.
In fact, it can be held that it is this uniqueness of the human
organism toward which all evolution moves. This is not to
say that we know that this is the end of evolution but, at
least, so far as we have gone along the pathway, this is the
outcome of evolution at present. This implies, as will be readily
seen, that evolution has had direction; that evolution has been
going somewhere, toward the development of uniquely different

individual living systems. The process, of course, has been fraught with trial and error. There have been many mistakes and there has been much wastage in the process. Because of this, many people deny the fact that evolution has direction, that it has been going anywhere. Many people seem to think that if they had had control of evolution they would have been able to think up better ways of getting the end result than wasting so much living material.

It follows from all this that human behavior is a complex, on the one hand, of inherited, automatic patterns controlled by the basal ganglia, and discriminative and rational behavior arising in the cortex, on the other. It is not surprising, therefore, that right at this point we run into one of the serious consequences of this particular kind of organization. Since the functions of the cortex derive not only from within the organism but also from the environment in which it lives, and because it can erect symbols and ideas out of all the stimuli, it is not surprising that in the course of cortical functioning, ideas should appear which cannot be carried out by the motor mechanisms, either of the cortex or of the basal ganglia. The cortex may demand too much of the automatic patterns of the more primitive brain. When it sends messages down the brain to the spinal cord, therefore, it runs into obstacles, finds conflicts. So also the automatic emotional functions of the basal ganglia may be so strong that they, spreading out over the cortex, come into conflict with the activities of the mind of man when the emotional, instinctive, automatic ways of solving problems are so strong that they tend to seek final control of man's behavior. There are times in all of our lives when the instinctive, emotional components of behavior bulk so large that they overwhelm the functionings of the cortex. This can be put into a little different language, for there is good evidence to suggest that the function of the basal ganglia, primarily, is to provide the drive, the impetus, in those kinds of motor activities which make the living system a going concern. On the other hand, the cortex can be thought of as the part of the nervous system which is primarily concerned with the goal toward which the whole organism reaches. Drives, therefore, can be in conflict with goals, and vice-versa. This, then, is the anatomy of anxiety, the conflict between discriminative, creative activities of the mind or cortex of man, on the one hand, and the automatic, inherited patterns of primitive behavior of the basal ganglia, on the other. Here is the seat of the mechanisms which are involved in conflict, frustration and anxiety. When the demands of the primitive neurones in the basal ganglia call for one kind of activity, and the discriminated, educable controls of the cortex call for another, there is almost certain to be confusion, conflict, and anxiety. People differ enormously in the relative domination of these two aspects of existence. Many people, a great deal of the time, behave as though all their activities were controlled by primitive mechanisms whereas, others behave, we hope, like generally rational beings. It must not be forgotten, however, that we can never be either completely rational nor emotional; we must be both.

The problem, if one accepts the analysis presented here is: how can we establish some kind of a balance between these two ways of determining behavior? So far as we know, there are no automatic neural connections to guarantee that such a balancing system is in existence. But the cortex, since it can learn, with its activities constantly changing, can develop and grow with experience. It is clear enough, when disease hits the cortex, or when neurosurgeons are compelled to remove parts of it, that profound changes in behavior result. Most of us are fairly well-oriented to our environment. We know where we are; we know the time of day; the day of the week or month, and similar ordinary things. But if, through diseases or surgery, the outlets from the cortex to the basal ganglia are obliterated, there is nearly always a profound change in the personality of the individual. He reverts to the animal. The individual is disoriented in time and place. He no longer is able to discriminate, nor to make adequate adjustment on anything but a purely physical level. The primitive controls of sex, hunger and fear dominate his picture. Some neurosurgeons even maintain that such individuals have lost their souls! This makes it quite clear that the functions of the cortex, in addition to providing uniqueness in behavior, also provide adequate regulation of the more primitive aspects of animal reactions to the physical environment. On the other hand, if the basal ganglia are involved in disease or in surgery, the results are nearly always catastrophic. The individual can rarely survive for any length of time if such neurones, controlling automatic behavior, are destroyed. There is a very interesting aspect of this interconnection between basal ganglia and cortex, because one of the astonishing things about nerve fibers is that though they are pre-determined quite early in both evolution and in development, they do not automatically become functionally mature just because they have established what seem to be adequate interconnections. There has to be a maturation process. This functional maturity does not reach its optimum of efficiency until the end of the second decade of life. This supposes, of course, that practice and experience — the business of living — help to activate the neural connections of this pathway to make them an important controlling factor in human behavior. Perhaps this is why the adolescent is so difficult to understand. The connections between his cortex and his basal ganglia are not functionally mature and, as a consequence, he is more animal than man. It can be argued further that some individuals in the population never acquire effective control through this functionally important connection between cortex and basal ganglia. It may well be that this is not a matter that can be taken care of by education or experience, but is one of the fundamental characters of an inherited pattern. Thus, again, the neural interconnections are always present, but their functional maturity can only be taught. Since all nerve cells are teachable, to some extent — they can all learn by practice and experience to perform their particular functions more efficiently — it would seem reasonable to conclude that the more adequate experience and training that the cortex gets, the greater the chance of proper balance between rational and primitive behavior. This implies, of course, that the effective functioning of the cortex, like many other pieces of apparatus, is dependent upon the kind of input to it; in other words, the kind of education which the cortex receives from the idealogical world. Although this has many advantages, there are, of course, many disadvantages. If we knew what this business of living were all about, it might be possible to set up environmental circumstances which would always result in the development of cortical controls in good and adequate balance with primitive controls. But, unfortunately, we do not know enough. We do not know why we are here, or what we are. We, therefore, fumble, try, fall into error and the result is that the problem of human relations is just as far from being solved today as it was in the beginning of man's career on the earth. Because he does not know all the answers, because he cannot figure out just what all the shooting is about, he tends to substitute for knowledge and wisdom pet schemes of his own to control most commonly other people's behavior, not his own. He forgets that he is a unique person and what may be entirely proper for him, is by no means adequate and proper for others. Moreover, since he does not know enough about the natural laws which, after all, determine the pattern of his nervous system, he can be quite certain to send down to the lower-lying centers of the nervous system orders which simply cannot be obeyed. If we knew enough, we could probably set up the right kind of educational procedure so that the bits of information which come into the cortex could be so organized, so controlled, that as the nervous system grows and matures, it would develop an adequate balance between reason and emotion. This is simply another way of saying, because of the unbelievable amount of information which pours into the human cortex in any one day, that the miracle of existence is that most of us are able to behave in a fairly adequate fashion. The commutations and permutations of all the stimuli which come to the cortex from the internal environment or from the outside world, are bound to lead to integrations which have to be tried out to see whether or not they will really work. Again, if we knew enough, hopefully, we would put into the cortex only the kind of information which would yield motor controls which make maximum use of the lower motor centers with minimum disturbance of the ordinary methods of controlling things. This means, of course, that we do not know enough about the nervous system. We do not know enough to be able to control the kind of information which goes into it so as to avoid the conflict between cortex and basal ganglia. And yet one of the strange things about human behavior is the fact that man spends a great deal of his time trying to control most commonly other people's behavior. Man thinks he can accomplish this by thinking up laws. The legalists, the lawyers, the legislators are continually writing laws about what the other fellow should do when there is no possible relationship between what the legalists call a necessary law and the factual functioning of the nervous system.

Nearly all of these man-made laws are to a greater or less extent in conflict with the laws which control the activities of the nervous system. Man knows a lot, but he does not know enough yet to be able to decide just exactly how the other fellow should behave. This is equally true of the religionists who have raised a series of regulations known as the moral law, which also has no relationship whatever to the forces which control the formation and the function of the human nervous system. Of course, we are anxious; of course, we are confused; of course, we are frustrated. Most of the troubles which man is heir to arise in the swamps of ignorance and stupidity. The unsolved problem of human relationships remains unsolved because we have spent so little time trying to find out how we can adjust the functions of the cortex in an harmonious fashion to the functions of the lower-lying parts of the nervous system. When these are related adequately in an internal harmony, we have the well-adjusted person; when they are not in internal harmony, we have all the variations and peculiar behavior which we recognize as the result of anxiety, frustration, and confusion. What is badly needed is for those who are involved in education, in the writing of laws, to relate all the information poured into the brain through eye and ear, to the basic functions of nerve cells whose position and connections are established before birth by Nature's powerful laws.

Chapter VIII

THE NATURE OF MAN

THE PRIMITIVE assumption of this discussion holds that the Universe is a unit, a whole. As such, it exhibits all the characteristics of an organization. It is composed of entities or regularities which can be identified and recognized. The familiar objects we see around us and in the heavens are such components. It matters not whether they be material things or wave phenomena, whether they be billiard balls of matter or the probability dance of electrical charges, they constitute the stuff of the Universe.

The fact that these units of stuff can be recognized and classified, that their combinations into groups are stable enough so that we can identify rocks, trees and animals, stars, planets, and galaxies, compels the belief that the units can be and are related to other entities by necessary relationships. Hence it can be held that the Universe is a place of Law and Order. The Law consists of those forces which impose the characteristic forms on nature — the precise, unbelievably powerful forces of attraction and repulsion, of Gravity and Universal Fields. We know that such things exist in what we perceive in the world around us, for by their means we can predict what will occur when two dissimilar chemials are placed in contact with each other, that two probability dances of hydrogen and one of oxygen, when brought together under the proper conditions, form water, a configuration whose properties are different from those of either component. We know that water is wet, that it can be frozen or boiled, that it can be converted into steam or vapor. We can establish, moreover, the necessary conditions to elicit these phenomena. In other words, we know the Laws which must be obeyed if any particular state of matter is to be achieved. All this is true of any recognizable state of nature that has been investigated up to the present.

We have discovered many of these laws. We have put them to work. The result is the unbelievable technological development of the last two centuries. None of the "things" we possess — electric lights and power, automobiles, planes, radios and the multitude of gadgets which make life pleasant, easy and altogether wonderful — would be possible without our knowledge and understanding of these laws. Science has done this for us, for it has sparked and made possible the technological achievements. Important as technology is, it follows from scientific understanding. Except by chance, gadgets do not discover fundamental principles.

Many argue that the above point of view is untenable, that in reality the prime characteristic of the Universe is chaos. Because we cannot be certain just where an electron is at any moment, because we cannot point and say, "that is an electron," it is held that there are no necessary laws involved in the basic constitution of Nature, except the laws of probability and of quanta of energy. The fact remains that though this be true at the ultra-microscopic level, there exist necessary relationships between probabilities which result in recognizable form and structure in Nature. We recognize trees when we see them, and also dogs, monkeys, and man. Certainly from a common-sense point of view, there are objects that can be described, stable states that exist in time and space and which involve energy transformations, in the midst of a constant flux of chemical change. To argue that such presentations of Nature are straight out of chaos, is to deny human experience.

On the contrary, it can be argued forcefully that all things we see and touch are the consequence of Law informing the entities, guiding and placing them. As a result, Order can be identified in the world around us and in the heavens above. The Universe *is* a place of Law and Order whose complexity can be understood by the mind of man.

But it is equally clear that the Universe is not static, rather it is a growing, changing unit, with matter and energy constantly shifting, yet always maintaining the wholeness. What was once thought to be characteristic only of living things, is now seen to be equally applicable to the whole Universe; old order changes giving place to new not only in civilizations on this minute speck, the earth, but also in the whole itself.

If all the above be granted, the central problem next to be solved is: What is the nature of the Law which establishes Order? This is the key question which is basic to all science — to all understanding of the Universe around us. Although this query has been raised since the dawn of thinking man, it has been largely ignored or stuck away in a dark corner of some tightly closed closet. A few courageous scientists, mainly mathematicians and astronomers, have dealt with the problem to our mutual benefit. But the largest body of observers dealing with it has been religionists, seers and prophets who have asserted that the answer has been found in the revelation to certain selected humans of a Divine Order. Unfortunately, such order has little or nothing to do with the Law and Order of the Universe. Rather, it is often in direct contradiction to it, to the everlasting confusion of mankind. It must not be forgotten, however, that the intuitive powers of the mind of man are manifold, so that many intuitions have been verified by science and by human experience. We ignore such flights of the imagination at our peril, for from them, sooner or later, come all of the advances of civilization.

There is a clue to the underlying force which establishes Law and Order. It is the electrical properties of Nature; for the most satisfactory definition of electricity is that it, electricity, is the way Nature behaves. All the evidence of modern atomic physics derives from the determined existence of electrical charges and their inter-relations. We believe in protons, electrons and all the other charged particles, in the electrical fields which bind them into necessary relatednesses. We believe in them so firmly that we put our knowledge about them into the creation of new and marvelous servants of man — into motors, lights, radio and radar, communication systems, automobiles and jets. Our knowledge of charges and fields makes it possible to produce indefinitely toasters and vacuum cleaners and to predict what missles and space ships will do in outer space. In other words, electricity has the properties and the characteristics demanded by the concept of the Law and Order in Nature.

The electrical field theory is highly successful when applied to the physical world — rocks and rills and the stars in the heavens. But is it applicable to the world of living things? Is life a special creation in this insignificant corner of an immense cosmos — in it, but not of it — planted on it, subject to many of the physical and chemical laws of Nature, but nevertheless transcending Nature? This is held by many. It demands the existence, in man at least, of something called the "soul" which is supposed to sit on the physical body of man and guide all of his activities. The soul is above physical law, reacting to what is called the moral law. It appears at some mysterious time and place in development, in the womb or at birth, or at maturity. It is presumed by many at least, to be external, to persist after the dissolution of the physical body. Existing in time, so far as it known, involving no energy transformations, located in no explicit part of human anatomy, it contradicts the entire concept of "Universe." For, if such a thing exists, then the Universe is not a unity but a duality — a physical universe and a spiritual universe. This is a straight negation of the meaning of the word Universe. This duality, moreover, implies the existence of two sets of determining factors, one transcending the other, one of a higher order, one capable of modifying physics and chemistry, at least, to suit its own convenience. What we are dealing with here is an indefensible construct growing out of the vanity of man. We like to believe that we are free — masters of our fate — but little lower than the angels. We cling blindly to an unverifiable assumption in order to support the idea of the dignity of man.

This notion of the duality of nature is nonsense. It is an unnecessary assumption, and yet it is quite obvious that man does possess a mind, a personality, a spirit, or a soul. We believe these things intuitively, even though we have as yet no proper evidence of their existence. They have not yet yielded to scientific investigation. We believe in them, nevertheless, and rightly, but *not* as some supernatural aspect of the world we know. Rather, they are qualitative attributes of the incredibly complex physical body of man. As redness is to the rose, so is mind to the nervous system; as hardness is to the rock, or softness to cotton, so is personality to the structure of man.

But as hardness does not make the rock, as mind does not make the nervous system, so these secondary consequences of the organization of the human being do not change you nor me. They are consequences, not causes. The driver does not change a Ford into a Lincoln. But, like a driver, the mind can channel the activities of the nervous system, give direction to its neural messages. It cannot put new neuronal components into the brain. All this is simply another way of saying that the intuitive mind, soul, needs no second transcendental world to explain or to justify it. It can be understood as the consequence of the discriminative, integrative, imaginitive functions of the human brain. But, as we have seen, the brain derives from the primary laws of nature working through chemicals and atoms and molecules, through stuff that is as common as table salt. And yet, what a miracle is man! From the simplest substances, the basic Laws of Nature make what is probably the most complex organization in the Universe, exceeded only by the Universe itself. If Nature's Laws can create organizations with such marvelous properties of thinking, loving, behaving, it is quite unnecessary to invent a transcendental world.

With an organized Universe, a place of Law and Order, we are faced with another problem that is no less formidable. What rational explanation can be given for the origin of such complex machines as man? It is impossible to find in our world a single instrument, machine, or gadget that has not been devised by the human mind. Only in Nature can we find complex organizations not of human origin. Every tool, every device used by man to increase his mastery of the environment, is designed. Dreamed of by someone's mind, developed and perfected by human skill and technical competence, they do not arise full-grown from chaos. Starting in the creative imagination of the mind, of a particular mind, they have been developed and perfected with the passage of time. In the design of the first wheeled vehicle, or in the first automobile, there is little that forecasts the modern Rolls-Royce, or the most recent Thunderbird. And yet, in retrospect, it is clear that the realization of the dream in modern times is made possible through a greater knowledge and understanding of Nature's Laws.

If our cosmologists are right, all this is true of the Universe. It had a beginning; it has grown and developed in time. New relationships have appeared, new organizations of charges created. Like man-made gadgets, the Universe is constantly changing, creating out of necessary relationships new energy transformations, new combinations of physical states. Only the religionists look upon the cosmos as a fixed, immutable, static affair. The Universe, moreover, like the automobile, provides clear-cut evidence that the whole, active, growing process has had direction and, therefore, is going somewhere. Equally clear is that it is science, sparked by the intuition and imagination of man's mind, that has made such understanding possible. In the same manner man, by means of his understanding, has put the same Laws of Nature to work, miraculously changing the world in which we live.

Since the Universe and all that therein lies, is a growing, developing design, the conclusion is inescapable that a Designer is at work. In the beginning was the Law and the Law was God. Needless to say, this concept of God as a Designer is at sharp variance with the Christian concept of a Deity. The notion of an all-powerful deity, sitting on the Universe and dictating every aspect of existence, interrupting Nature's Laws at will to satisfy the pleas of properly oriented humans, is absurd. Such a stultifying, dogmatic, authoritarian picture of God is hardly tenable in the face of the evidence. It precludes the possibility of change. There is no room in it for the exciting, stimulating, and almost explosive aspects of the cosmos. God is the Designer, working always toward a better Universe, but working always through the Laws which He established. Like every creative mind, He constantly seeks new ways of building a more perfect Universe.

Now Man is an integral part of this design. He was not born in chaos. He is a designed instrument of God, working with Him, travelling with Him the road to, for us, an unseen goal. That there is an object to all this cannot be doubted. Since you and I do not know everything, we cannot see the goal. but that is exists, is inescapable.

It follows from all this that Man, as a designed instrument of God, is a cooperator with God in the developing Universe. His cooperation becomes more and more effective as he knows and understands better the complexity of organization of the cosmos. You will ask, "How can Man be that good?" Of course, he is not, but he can work toward it. Since, moreover, Man is made up of all the qualitative attributes, all of the functions of his nervous system; and since all of these are products of the basic laws of the Universe, it follows that by no chance can he operate outside these laws, even though moralists and legalists often demand such behavior. Those laws have made him. He exists because of them. The ancient intuition which asserts that, "Closer is He than breathing and nearer than hands and feet," is a solid fact. He, Man, as a designed nervous system, has grown and developed from the simplest stuff of living matter. He is not the accidental conglomeration of chemicals spawned in chaos. The whole, long history of evolution has had direction. As far as we have gone along the road, it would seem that the goal of evolution has had direction. As far as we have gone along the road, it would seem that the goal of evolution has been the appearance of the unique, human individual. Thus, Man is the functioning of a complex nervous system, known to us through his behavior, and exhibiting characteristics to which we have given such names as Mind, Soul, Spirit, Personality, Character. As a uniquely organized collection of living nerve cells, he possesses unique abilities, special capacities for performing particular jobs. Thus, there are artists, musicians, writers, workers with hands and minds, each peculiarly fitted to achieve certain goals.

There is one difficulty, of course, in this set-up. The capacities of every human brain are so manifold that many, perhaps most, of us can never make up our minds what we want to do. So many things are interesting that it is difficult to discover the nature of the work we are designed to do best. This is the reason, of course, why education must have a broad base, offering the growing child samples of many ways of life. Competence, however, does not grow just from interest alone; it requires disciplined practice, repetition of behavior patterns until they become truly effective. Unfortunately, most of us get discouraged before disciplined practice becomes the self-discipline which alone leads to successful behavior.

So far as it known, the most reliable clue to the nature of the job each of us is best fitted to perform, is the answer to the question: If I could do exactly what I want to do, without limitations or restrictions, what would it be? In other words, what would I rather do than eat? Discover that and you will be made; you will be an active and successful cooperator with the Designer. This demands some sacrifices, of course. Some activities must be endured so that other more important things can be accomplished.

To many, the above will sound dogmatic, authoritarian, arguing that the fate of man is pre-determined. Well, it is — but also, it is not. It is, because no one of us can put new nerve cells nor new connections into the organization of the nervous system. But the stock of possible kinds of behavior is so enormous that, given intuition and imagination, many, but not any kind, of competence, can be achieved within the framework of the given neural organization. Artists, musicians, mathematicians are born, and are made through the disciplined practice of neural nets inherent in the individual. If your neural organization is such that you have no interest in music, no amount of practice will make you a musician. But if you have a particular plan of neural combinations so that you have a driving interest in some aspect of the business of living, there seems to be almost no limit to where you can go.

As designed instruments of God, therefore, it behooves us to know ourselves; to discover, through our interests, our abilities and then to get at them, for we are working partners in a scheme that staggers our imagination. That there is such a plan cannot be doubted, even though we see through a glass darkly the bare outlines of its framework. Thus, life becomes for each of us an exciting, glorious, and adventuresome journey.

Chapter IX

THE MEANING OF EXISTENCE

BUT MANY will say — none of this defines in an explicit way the nature of man as an individual, as a significant entity in the immensity of the Universe. When the question is asked: What Is Man? — a particular, unique description is demanded. Unfortunately, most of us want a short, easily understood formula whose solution would require no thought nor effort on our part. We want a pretty, easily digested pill that will solve our problems and cure us of all ills. We would like to have someone else do the work, so that we could sit back and relax. But this is not in the nature of things nor of the Universe. All living is a game of giving and taking. From one point of view, life is a struggle; a constant activity aimed always at coming to some kind of terms with the world around us.

In the case of man, this means adjusting not only to our physical surroundings but also to our idealogical environment, for Life is never static; it is always going somewhere. The trouble is that for so many the "where" is unknown; for too many, there is no conviction that it exists. This is the real, the major difficulty. Not knowing what he is nor where he is going, mankind lives a day-to-day existence — "sufficient unto the day," and so on. Having no goals, no direction to his behavior, he drifts through life more or less content with the daily grind. It is not surprising, therefore, that there is so much apparent dissatisfaction, so much anxiety, so many frequent breakdowns of our human relationships. As a result, peoples and nations squabble, worry about prestige or status, not only of themselves, but also of the particular group or race or nation to which they belong. Looking at the way humans behave, no wonder the people cry, "Chaos, all is Chaos!"

How footless, fruitless and silly this point of view is. We

are all alive; we are designed components of a designed Universe. We cannot escape it, try as hard as we may. To shut our eyes to the Universal Law which, after all, is the language of God, is just as dangerous as it would be to leap from the top of the nearest tall building, or the nearest mountain top. So long as we live, we must play ball according to the rules. And there is the rub! We do not know all the rules. We have learned enough so that most of us stay alive and reasonably well. We avoid poisons, infections and accidents of many kinds almost automatically, for most of the techniques by which these are accomplished are taken care of by the marvelous efficiency of the nervous system. But, Man, as a uniquely designed part of the Universe, has been endowed with neural networks which give him capacities of thinking, dreaming, and doing which transcend even his own imagination. In many ways, it looks as though there were almost no limit to what man could accomplish. He can do all these things, not because of a supernatural soul or spirit or mind, but because his nervous system, his brain, has made it possible through constant search, through "blood, sweat and tears," to uncover Nature's or God's way of doing things. Man does not create; he discovers. As a result, certainly all the things he makes are made possible by his increasing knowledge and understanding of Natural Law. By virtue of the billions of nerve cells in his brain, man is an entity, a whole, a being who can, by working with Nature, build complex chemicals, machines, computers, all of which Nature has already fashioned more beautifully.

That there is a meaning to the Universe, cannot be gainsaid. The difficulty lies in the fact that we cannot finally define the meaning. To do so would require infinite knowledge and understanding. Each new fact validated by science, each new glimpse of unsuspected relationship envisaged by the imagination of the mind of man, each new beauty seen or heard, draws us nearer to understanding. Thus, existence is an exciting journey, an adventure into the unknown.

Like all adventures, however, a goal is required. The explorer traversing the ice to the South Pole, or the climber seeking the top of the highest mountain, cannot define the objective in detail. He believes that such things exist, but his knowledge is limited. Making use of a background of past information, and recruiting imagination and understanding, he pushes on toward the unknown. So you and I gather as many facts as possible, glimpse new relationships and, through greater understanding, move slowly and hesitantly to greater harmony with the Universe.

It is easy to write this. Harmony is exceedingly difficult to achieve. But who of us would like it if we knew all the answers, had no problems to solve? Some there are who long for peace, where there is no more struggle, no more unsolved equations. To desire this is stultifying. It is a denial of the nature of the Universe. If life were that easy, where would be the fun?

Since all living, moreover, is a constant adaptation of every living organism, from mice to man, to the constantly changing world, both within and without, and since such adjustment is made possible only through the functions of brain and nerve, the more we can learn about the nervous system and, therefore, ourselves, the greater is the likelihood of progress toward the goal of the Universe. As a matter of fact, the only stuff we have to work with is discovered by the functioning of the human brain. It behooves us, then, as the prime requisite for any grasp of the meaning of existence, to learn all we can about this mechanism which keeps us alive, in both the physical sense and the realm of ideas. Fortunately, Nature, or the basic laws of the Universe, has taken care of adaptation to the material world about us. The machinery of the older parts of the brain have been refined by the long practice and experience of the developing evolution of living things. The result is a marvelously efficient mechanism — one that can be trusted to do its job under widely varying circumstances. It is so good that we rely on it without question. We interfere with it at our peril!

The "we" who pokes a monkey-wrench into the works is, of course, the marvelous gray matter of the brain. But this is a relatively recent addition to the biology of living beings.

It has not had the kind of rigorous conditioning that has made the areas of the brain concerned with the physical world so effective. The Designer of the Universe, like human designers, has had a goal and has had, like human beings, to modify the design as a result of experience. That Man, in his designs, has not been so successful as the Great Designer, results from our inadequate concept and understanding of the Great Design. Man, using what he knows of the Laws of the Universe, has had to develop his designs. The basic principles of all motor vehicles have been constant in time, but the designs most certainly have changed and developed to produce more effective results. There has been apparent waste in such change and growth, just as there has been in the program of evolution. One feels inclined to ask, if the Designer is really omnipotent, why did He not start out with a perfect design? The answer would seem to be clear. A perfectly designed and working Universe would be static, frozen, dogmatic, and authoritarian, and completely uninteresting and unexciting. With no problems to solve, the whole Universe and all of mankind would be condemned to a frozen existence. And who wants that? Certainly not the Designer; surely not Man!

All we know about the Universe and its design is the result of the functioning of our brains. Although each brain is uniquely individual, there are, nevertheless, generalities in its activities which make it possible to recognize generalities in Nature, describable regularities in the continuum of Nature. By bits of information sent through the senses, the brain discriminates, integrates, coordinates in what seem to be new ways, symbols, pictures, understandings of Nature. But since each brain is uniquely different, every approach to the Universe is individually ordered, true in detail only for that particular nervous system yet, nevertheless, characterized by generalities common to all human brains, independent of race, color, or nationality.

It should be evident that there cannot be one meaning to existence. Rather, the meanings are as varied as the brains which seek them. Each brain discovers its own. What is an adequate meaning for me, moreover, may or may not be significant for you. It follows, therefore, that the meaning of existence is that it has meaning — describable, reproducible, predictable characteristics. For you and me, this affirms that the business of living in a designed Universe is to enlarge, continually, our knowledge and understanding of that design. This must be an act of faith. But we live by faith — that the sun will rise to-morrow — that pressure on a button will start the motor — that there is a route by which we may travel from here to London, Paris, Hong-Kong. We believe these things to be true. The evidence convinces us. So also, the evidence we believe about the nature of the Universe, compels the conviction that the Universe is a place of Law and Order that man can learn to understand.

All this puts a tremendous burden on the gray matter of the brain for, through it alone, are the myriad bits of information selected, compared and converted into that behavior which, through practice and experience, can be validated, can be found to work. Moreover, since much of the information poured into the brain comes from other brains, a considerable degree of selection of the kind and quality of ideas received, arises in the educational and cultural environment. This is one of the facts which makes for difference in people. The influx of ideas, however, meets certain nerve networks with which it is compatible, particular combinations of neurones which react most appropriately to such ideas. Thus the business of education is to provide, hopefully, the specific brain with the kind of idealogical environment in which can result in the most efficient operation of those neural nets, of that unique gray matter.

The search for meaning, then, is an exploration of the possible capacities of the mind — it must be remembered that these are manifold — and the kind of ideas which can most effectively be realized in behavior. Such an adventure is fraught with excitement, dogged by many pitfalls, wasteful in the apparent dissipation of energy, yet an adventure which dwarfs all others. It requires the maximum possible knowledge and understanding of the pattern of organization of the brain, and greater comprehension of its functioning. So much is to be learned; so little is known. Within the designed frame-work of the Universe, there is a goal. Each of us must seek it individually; each of us must cross the valley alone — and yet not alone — for as designed parts of the whole, we are vital and important tools of God.